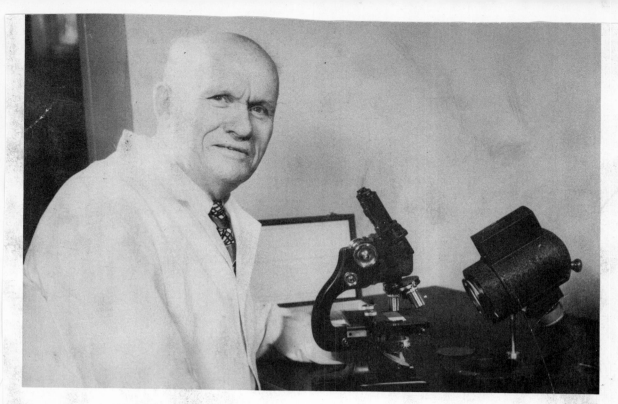

Meet the Author

It can safely be claimed that CARL GOTTFRIED HARTMAN knows more about the opossum than any other man who has ever lived. Throughout a long and distinguished career as a scientist, his investigations into the nature and habits of this strange animal have continued. The end result is this book.

A native of Iowa, Dr. Hartman holds the first Ph.D. degree ever granted by the University of Texas. He is a former professor of zoology and physiology at the Universities of Texas and Illinois, and is now Associate Director of the Ortho Research Foundation at Raritan, N. J.

Frequent lecturer in major European universities, Dr. Hartman was in 1946 given the Squibb Award by the Society for the Study of Internal Secretions, and in 1948 received the coveted Lasker Award from the Planned Parenthood Federation of America. He is the author of six books in the fields of endocrinology and physiology and of more than 200 articles in scientific journals.

POSSUMS

POSSUMS

CARL G. HARTMAN

UNIVERSITY OF TEXAS PRESS. AUSTIN

1952

UNIVERSITY OF TEXAS PRESS
Austin 12

THOMAS NELSON AND SONS LTD

Parkside Works   Edinburgh 9
3 Henrietta Street   London WC2
312 Flinders Street   Melbourne C1
5 Parker's Buildings   Burg Street   Cape Town

Thomas Nelson and Sons (Canada) Ltd
91-93 Wellington Street West   Toronto 1

Société Française d'Editions Nelson
25 rue Henri Barbusse   Paris V^e

To My Wife
Eva Rettenmeyer Hartman
for much help in compiling and
sifting the historical data
used in this book

Contents

Illustrations

POSSUMS

Introduction

AMERICA has two strange beasts native to the soil. They are the opossum and the armadillo. The latter, a recent migrant from Mexico, has not acquired the aura of legend, song, and story which surrounds the opossum. Moreover, the armadillo's most peculiar trait, the production, at each parturition, of quadruplets which are always of the same sex, is of rather academic interest and little susceptible to mystical interpretation.

This leaves the opossum as the strangest of all our native species. *"Animal mirabile,"* exclaimed Ralph Hamor in 1610; in 1649, Lawson echoed: "She is the wonder of all animals."

The opossum is the first pouch-bearer with which Western civilization came in contact. Born a veritable embryo and incubated in the abdominal pouch, the opossum has been a source of wonderment and conjecture ever since the year 1500. In that year the explorer Pinzón picked up, in newly discovered Brazil, a female opossum with young in her pouch. Pinzón brought her to Spain, where he presented her to the astonished monarchs Ferdinand and Isabella, who placed their royal fingers in the pouch and marveled at so strange a contrivance of Nature.

For a whole century of Spanish discovery and conquest, New Spain furnished material for sensational contributions to natural history and also to nature-faking on a grand scale. In these the opossum played a spectacular role. With the settlement of Virginia, the English were in a position further to popularize the opossum, and it was Captain John Smith who wrote the first description in English of the "Virginia" opossum and bestowed upon it the Indian name, *opossum,* by which it is now known.

Almost a century passed before the French reached the land of the *rat de bois* in New France or Louisiana, for they had to travel far, coming by way of the St. Lawrence and the Great Lakes, the Illinois and the Mississippi rivers. About a century after La Salle planted the tricolor of France at the mouth of the Mississippi, a whole host of close relatives of the opossum (kangaroos, wombats, bandicoots, and scores of others) became known when Captain James Cook and his scientific staff landed on the east coast of "New Holland," now known as Australia, opening up to the world of science an island-continent of biological wonders and (till then) missing links in the evolutionary scale of life.

Today there exist no marsupials or pouched animals in Eurasia, Africa, Java, Sumatra, or the Philippines. They are to be found only in the Americas and in Australia, Tasmania, and

Four species of opossum. Upper row: Didelphis marsupialis, *probably the species first seen by a white man (Pinzón, 1500); and* Metachirus nudicaudatus, *locally known as* mucura ixica. *Bottom row:* Metachirops; *and young Virginia opossum, photographed by Robert Hatt. The three other photographs were taken by G. W. D. Hamlett in Pará, Brazil.*

some of the islands to the north. This limited distribution did not always obtain; for hundreds of millions of years before the advent of the higher mammals, marsupials roamed over all the land masses. This we have known ever since Cuvier in 1820 discovered marsupial fossils in the gypsum of the streets of Paris.

The mystery of the development, birth, and marsupial gestation of the opossum challenged the imagination and evaded solution for four centuries. The major questions involved finally yielded to the simple method of careful, direct observation, which is the essence of science. Since circumstances were such that I could scarcely escape playing the role of pioneer possum embryologist and accoucheur, I have written this book to make more readily available the facts concerning marsupial life. That the facts themselves are

interesting enough was the opinion of the Rev. J. G. Wood, who stated in his popular *Animate Creation:* "Many of the creatures, such as the kangaroo and some of the opossums, are so remarkable in their habits of life, that if they had not been made familiar to us through the medium of menageries, museums, and the writings of accredited travellers, we should be inclined to consider them and their habits to be but the emenations from the fertile brain of some imaginary voyager, who was taking full advantage of the proverbial travellers' license."

Along with assembling and adding to authenticated facts concerning marsupial life, I have occupied myself from time to time tracking down to their origins the fanciful ideas and fantastic explanations of natural phenomena which early travelers gathered from aborigines or which they themselves in-

2

This steel engraving of South American mammals was used as a headpiece in Buffon's famous Histoire naturelle, générale et particulière *(1749). Left: peccary, armadillo, and sloth. Center: giant anteater and (on mantel) a pair of squirrels and a pair of opossums* (Didelphis marsupialis). *Right: pangolin, partly hiding mouse opossum with young attached to teats, and two vampire bats.*

vented. Not only was such nature lore perpetuated from one generation of writers to another, but European travelers and explorers transferred to the New World animal legends originating on the Eurasian continent, and of course still current there. As Folklorist J. Frank Dobie tells us in his *Voice of the Coyote* (1950): "Some tales belong to all races—no matter what their origin. If they have vitality, they take the first ship out to travel across oceans and fasten themselves to fresh hosts." The opossum was especially well adapted to become host to such imported legends.

The warp of the story told in this book will consist of facts established by careful observation and painstaking experiment in the modern manner; the woof will be made up of fables, folklore, legends, and pseudo science. These two phases will be presented *pari passu* as the essay unfolds.

Because the opossum is common in our Southland, this denizen of the woods is traditionally linked with the American Negro; but the legendary and bizarre beliefs about Br'er Possum are a part of the heritage of all Southerners, regardless of race or degree of sophistication. Being both common and unique, the opossum has inspired more poetry of the people than has any other animal. Specimens of this literature, as well as a few samples of Negro and Indian folklore, are included.

Since the literary descriptions of the opossum called for pictorial representation, often by artists of the first rank, the illustrations in this volume constitute a brief history of animal-illustrating. The selections range from woodcuts from early maps, books of travel, and textbooks of zoology, through the more elegant copper and steel engravings, to lithographs and modern photographic halftones.

It is hoped that this not too technical or too serious account will increase interest in this unique, albeit extremely stupid, species of animal indigenous to our soil.

3

Title page of Charles César Rochefort's book, copied from the 1665 edition. Here Louis XIV is shown receiving Indians bringing some of the products of their country, including an opossum.

1

Europeans Meet the Opossum

It was Vicente Yáñez Pinzón who, of all western Europeans, was the first to hold in his hand a marsupial animal and to discover the marsupial pouch.

Pinzón had captained the *Niña,* one of Columbus' caravels, and so had taken part in the discovery of the New World. Jealous of the "foreigner" Columbus, Pinzón thenceforth headed his own three expeditions. It was on the first of these that he crossed the Equator (for the first time in western seas) and on January 28, 1500, sighted the coast of what is now Brazil. On February 8 he landed, and "at the base of a tree which sixteen men could scarcely span" he found a mother opossum with young in the pouch. Realizing that here was a novelty unfamiliar to the Old World, he brought the animal back to Spain, where the "incredible mother" was presented at the court of Ferdinand and Isabella.

Although Spaniards were the chief actors in this scene, it remained for two Venetians to make the strange beast known to Europeans, who, since the voyage of Columbus, were avid for news from the expanding world.

For several centuries Venice had been the wealthy mistress of the Mediterranean, growing rich on the trans-Asiatic caravan trade as well as profiteering at the expense of the Crusaders. But the days of her ascendancy were

numbered; for after Ferdinand expelled the last of the Moors and Columbus opened a new empire for the King, the Spaniards as well as the equally bold Portuguese were destined for a time to play a dominant role as world powers. Their rise was already assured when Vasco da Gama rounded the Cape of Good Hope and discovered the water route to the East Indies. The final blow to Venetian business came when Cabral, in 1501, returned from Calcutta with a shipload of spices, which he was able to lay down in Lisbon at 2 per cent of the price fixed by the trust-ridden Venetians.

So it came about that the Venetian "Chamber of Commerce" or its equivalent, jittery at the prospect of financial losses, sent an observer to Madrid, the world's most important listening post. This agent reported regularly by letter on the movements of the Spanish and the Portuguese in world trade. His name was Angelo Trevigliano.

At the same time there lived in Madrid another Venetian, Pietro Martire d'Anghiera, better known as Peter Martyr. He did not represent business, but rather the Church, of which he was a devout member. From early youth he had been an associate of poets and scholars of Rome and Venice. He was littérateur, reporter, historian, priest, soldier, and

5

diplomat. Most of his life was spent at the Spanish court, first as secretary to the Venetian ambassador, later in the service of the king.

Peter Martyr recognized the significance of the discovery of America, knew personally most of the *voyageurs* of the day, and wrote about their discoveries. Since he took his stories directly from the mouths of the returning heroes, his writings have all the flavor of firsthand information, including all the exaggerations with which adventurers of the day embellished their tales. It is more than likely that Peter Martyr interviewed Pinzón and his crew, for he wrote of asking the sailors if they had seen the southern polar star, to which they replied that they had not but that the southern constellations were different from those of the north.

From the pen of Peter Martyr a steady stream of letters went from Spain to Venice. These letters, written in Latin, numbered over eight hundred and were embodied in his world-famous *De Orbe Novo decades*. This covered the period from 1493 to the time of his death, in 1526. He dedicated his *Decades* to Cardinal Sforza; they were passed around for reading and became the subject of conversation in universities and palaces. After Peter Martyr's death the letters were continued by Montalboddo.

While it is certain that it was Peter Martyr who gathered the story of the opossum, Trevigliano beat him to the publication of it. The story appeared in Trevigliano's *Libretto di tutta la navigatione* in 1504, twelve years before Peter Martyr published (in the Ninth Book of his First Decade) the account of the voyage of Pinzón and the discovery of the opossum. That Peter Martyr resented the "theft" is indicated by the following passage in a later decade in which he refers to the previously described opossum: "There is also an animal which lives in the trees, feeds upon fruits, and carries its young in a pouch in the belly; no writer as far as I know has seen it,

but I have already sufficiently described it in the Decade which has already reached Your Holiness before your elevation, as it was then stolen from me to be printed."

The *Decades* were translated into many languages and were popular for a century or more. Sebastian Münster copied liberally from them in his *Cosmographiae*, and the Italian seventeenth-century version by Girolamo Benzoni was well known around 1800 to our own Dr. Benjamin Smith Barton of Philadelphia.

Two renditions of the section of the decade dealing with the opossum illustrate the use made of the meager knowledge then available and the slowness with which scientific information spread even in the Renaissance. The first quotation is from Richard Eden's *The Decades of the Newe Worlde or West India* (1555, edited by Arber, 1885), a work which, by the way, was read by William Shakespeare.

They affirme that there are trees of suche byggenes, that .xvi. men joyninge handes togyther and standinge in coompasse, can scarsely embrase sum of them. Emonge these trees is fownde that monstrous beaste with a snowte lyke a foxe, a tayle lyke a marmasette, eares lyke a batte, handes lyke a man, and feete lyke an ape, bearing her whelpes abowte with her in an owtwarde bellye much lyke unto a great bagge or purse. The deade carkas of this beast, you sawe with me, and turned it over and over with yowre owne handes, marveylynge at that newe belly and wonderfull provision of nature. They say it is knowen by experience, that shee never letteth her whelpes goo owte of that purse, except it bee eyther to play, or to sucke, untyl suche tyme that they bee able to gette theyr lyving by them selves. They tooke this beaste with her whelpes: But the whelpes dyed shortely after in the shyppes. Yet the damme lived certeyne moonethes: But at the length, not beinge able to abyde soo great alteration of ayer, and chaunge of meate, shee dyed also in the way. But of this beaste, wee have sayde enowgh.

The second quotation is from the German edition of Peter Martyr, published in 1582 by

Earliest representation of the opossum, from Waldseemüller's world map of 1516. For translation of legend in box see text.

Nicolaus H. von Königshofer. There follows a free translation of the pertinent passage, under the heading "The Animal with Two Bellies":

Under this unbelievably thick tree they [Pinzón and his men] found a frightful animal which possesses a muzzle like a fox, a tail like a monkey, ears like a bat, and human hands similar to those of monkeys, which animal carries its young about when foraging for food. It has below on the belly a second belly hanging down like a great sack or pouch. This animal, though it was dead, I demonstrated to Your Royal Highness, together with the sack of the new belly and the unheard-of means of nature by which the mother protects its young against flesh-eating and predaceous animals; and you placed your hands into this pouch and marveled greatly thereat. Many observations have shown that this animal carries its young in the sack of the belly wherever it goes and never lets them out except to suckle them or otherwise refresh or rest them until they are grown and able to secure food and nourishment through their own strength and protect themselves against the attacks of other animals by

their own strength. We captured an animal with young, but the young soon died on shipboard though the mother lived several months, finally dying because it could not endure the change of food and air. Of this animal we have now spoken enough and we shall return to the discoverer of these things.

Through these writings the civilized world was made aware of a new type of animal life. Zoological science had, however, not yet advanced sufficiently to comprehend the opossum as anything more than just another strange beast.

In this chapter of "firsts" it seems fitting to present also the first pictorial representation of the opossum. This picture is to be found in the lower left-hand corner of Waldseemüller's world map of 1516 (but not on his earlier map). The illustration here reproduced is the prototype of pictures of the opossum current for almost two centuries. The Latin inscription accompanying the woodcut I translate as follows: "There is shown in this picture

7

The opossum (and cannibals) from the Ptolemy map of 1522. The legend under the woodcut of the opossum is similar to that on the Waldseemüller map.

this animal which has a receptacle under its belly in which it carries its young except when it puts them out to suckle. The same was shown to the Spanish king in the city of Granada." The reader will recognize Peter Martyr here.

In the upper right-hand corner of the same picture it is stated that the opossum is found in the land of cannibals. The Ptolemy map of 1522, as the reader may see, also has the same effigy of the animal, facing to the right, however. The artist in this case improved on Waldseemüller by adding crude sketches of cannibals gnawing on human arms and legs.

From the Waldseemüller model Gesner had his engraver sketch the opossum for his famous zoology, although this author expressed regret that he had to describe the beast entirely on the authority of others. The Latin Gesner of 1558 and the German edition by Forer (1563) were illustrated by woodcuts, but Johnston's English version (1657) by copper engravings, then coming into vogue. As was the custom before the days of copyright, Johnston's artist camouflaged the plagiarism somewhat by having his *simivulpa* face opposite to that in the original.

All of these early picturizations of the opos-sum have in common a factual error in that the pouch was placed under the chest instead of over the teats. The mistake arose, one may surmise, from the statement in Peter Martyr's original description that the dam was supposed to let the young out of the pouch to suckle. Aldrovandi (1637) and Johnston (1657) and other famous authors continued to perpetuate the old interpretation, in pictures as well as text, although by their time more exact descriptions had been published. Fra Sahagún, for example, having lived in Mexico for many years after the Conquest and having seen many opossums in the flesh, was able to sketch mother and pouch young in their correct relations. More accessible to European writers than Sahagún's account was that in Hans Stade's autobiographical story of his captivity among the cannibals of the Amazon country. In his book he described the opossum quite realistically, and his picture of the *serwoy* (another Indian word for "opossum") was very creditable for the sixteenth century. Stade wrote:

There is also a kind of game, called Serwoy, which is as large as, and which has a tail like, a cat; its hair is whitish-grey, and also blackish-grey. And when it breeds it bears about six young,

8

and it has a slit in the belly, about half a span in length. Within the slit there is yet another skin; for its belly is not open, and within this slit are the teats. Wherever it goes, it carries its young in the slit between the two skins. I have often helped to catch them, and have pulled the young ones from out of the slit.

The foregoing and many other citations of faulty observation and fanciful deductions by the early travelers in the New World are not made in a spirit of *post hoc* disparagement of their efforts. Rather, one must view them as did Thomas Jefferson in one of his controversial essays published in *Notes on the State of Virginia* (1781–82), where he wrote: "But who were these travellers [who brought back reports of animal life in America]? . . . Was natural history the object of their travels? . . . Were they acquainted with the animals of their own country, with which they undertake to compare them?"

Of further contributions to opossum lore made by the Spaniards it must suffice to list only some of those that came out of Mexico soon after its conquest by Cortez. While the Spanish friars destroyed much cultural material of the pagan Aztecs, men like Fra Sahagún, who lived in Mexico for sixty years, rescued some of the nature lore of Montezuma's kingdom, including their highly developed materia medica. This was so advanced that Cortez warned King Philip II that any Spanish physicians whom he might send would be embarrassed by the superior knowledge of the Aztec medicine men. However, Francisco Hernández, physician to the King, spent six years in Mexico, where he knew Sahagún and wrote seventeen volumes of observations. These were largely lost in a fire in Madrid in 1671; but Francisco Jiménez, who lived in Mexico soon after Sahagún's death, seems to have been the one who preserved for posterity some of the herbals and recipes, including those extolling the wonderful virtues of concoctions of the opossum tail. As the medical lore dates back to Sahagún,

I quote first from Del Campo's analysis of Sahagún's writings:

Finally, mention is made of the medicinal properties of the tail of the *tlacuache* [Aztec for "opossum"]. "It has great medicinal value: it draws out, through many applications, any ailment of the flesh or bone; and women who are in labor, if they drink a little of the steeped tail of this animal, give birth immediately; those who are constipated are cured at once by drinking a little of the extract because it opens and cleanses the pores; those who have a cough get well by drinking this broth."

Later travelers and writers on natural history of the various regions copied the Sahagún-Hernández-Jiménez recipes and even improved on them. One of these was Georg Marcgrave, who, with the physician Willem Piso, resided in the Dutch colony in Brazil from 1638 to 1644. Astronomer, botanist, and naturalist, Marcgrave made a good start in the study of Brazil's flora and fauna. I quote a choice passage from Marcgrave as it was rendered (partially) from the Latin by Dr. John D. Godman in his quite creditable *American Natural History* (1846):

The tail of this animal is a singular and wonderful remedy against inflammation of the kidney; for if it be broken, and the quantity of a drachm of the water in which it is steeped be drunk sometimes, fasting, it wonderfully cleanses the ureters, expels calculi and other obstructions (excitat venerem, et generat lac, medetur colicis doloribus prodest parientibus et accelerat partum, promovet menses) and if it be chewed and placed on the part into which thorns have been thrust, it extracts them, loosens the bowels, and I believe in all New Spain there is not to be found another remedy as useful in so many cases.

The Latin portion of the quotation I have let stand as Godman wrote it as an example of a custom among writers of a century ago, before the enlightened age of Kinsey, when matters of sex were stated in Latin in order to conceal their meaning from all but the learned. This portion of the passage just quoted may be rendered thus: "It excites

9

lust and generates milk, reduces labor pains and hastens birth, regulates the menses." Dr. Godman might have spared me the trouble; yet he has given me an opportunity to dilate on one of the eccentricities of his age, namely the prudery which flourished in America more than in any other country in the world.

The several writings above suffice to give some idea of the part played by the Spaniards in discovering and making known to the philosophical world a hitherto unheard-of method of reproduction among mammals. It required a century for the English, and almost an additional century for the French, to come to know this unusual creature, the opossum.

The first settlements of the English in the New World happen to have been made near the northern range of opossums, the home of the species now called Virginia opossum. The

Above: woodcut from Forer (1563). Below: copper engraving from Johnston (1657).

10

best-known and most quoted descriptions of the animal stem from Captain John Smith and other settlers who published their accounts soon after the founding of the Jamestown Colony in 1607. Of the opossum Captain John Smith wrote in his *True Relation* (1608): "An Opassom hath an head like a Swine, and a taile like a Rat, and is of the bignes of a Cat. Under her belly she hath a bagge, wherein shee lodgeth, carrieth, and sucketh her young."

The secretary of the Jamestown Colony, William Strachey, in his *Historie of Travaile into Virginia Britannia* (1610, 1611, 1612), published the following description: "An opussum is a beast as big as a pretty beagle, of grey cullour; yt hath a head like a swyne, eares, feet and tayle like a ratt; she carries her young ones under her belly, in a piece of her own skyn, like as in a bagg, which she can open and shutt, to let them out or take them in, as she pleaseth, and doth therein lodge, carry, and suckle her young, and eates in tast like a pig."

To another Virginian, Ralph Hamor, the opossum was nature's *animal mirabile:* "The Apossums not unlike a month old pig in size and shape, is a stocky animal of most unbelievable nature 'animal mirabile', she gives birth to seven young at a time, more or less, which she hides in her belly until they have attained a month's growth, when she sends them forth a second time except in time of danger to herself or her offspring."

These writers of the Jamestown Colony were anticipated by a score of years, however, by a most competent Englishman, the mathematician and naturalist Thomas Harriot. This man made substantial contributions to the science of algebra and was, incidentally, a tutor to Sir Walter Raleigh. It was logical, therefore, that Sir Walter should appoint him, in 1585, surveyor to the colony established on Roanoke Island. Harriot's book, *A Briefe and True Report of the New Found Land of Virginia,* was better executed than those written

Sketch copied from the Florentine Codex (Book XI, Pl. 77, Fig. 21), which deals with early Mexican history. The original has a landscape in the background.

by mere explorers of the day. Harriot's artist, John White, made many on-the-spot sketches. These he showed to the famous copper-engraver De Bry on the occasion of the latter's visit, in London, to the historian Richard Hakluyt, whose books of travel De Bry was illustrating. As a result of this meeting with White, De Bry later brought out an edition of Harriot's book in Frankfurt, illustrating it with copper engravings in the best style of the De Bry family of artists.

In numerous works on the natural history of Virginia and the Carolinas published in the seventeenth and eighteenth centuries, the opossum is given prominence, and descriptions of its appearance and habits gradually improve; at the same time, the treatises bring in fanciful conjectures concerning the generation of the animal. There was a tendency, however, among writers on the natural history of Virginia to copy from one another. Brickell, for example, lifted from Lawson's book the description of the opossum almost word for word, even to the statement that "if a cat has nine lives, this creature surely has nineteen; for if you break every bone in their skin, and mash their skull, leaving them for dead, you may come an hour after, and they are gone."

Among the writers of this period the most competent scientist was Mark Catesby, a fellow of the Royal Society. As the following quotation shows, he was circumspect in his conclusions, questioning some of the false notions current at the time:

But what is most remarkable in this Creature and different from all others, is its false Belly, which is formed by a Skin or Membrane (including its Dugs), which it opens and closes at Will. Though contrary to the Laws of Nature, nothing is more believed in America than that these Creatures are bred at the Teats by their Dams: But as it appeared from the Dissection of one of them by Dr. Tyson, that their Structure is formed for Generation like that of any other Animals, they must necessarily be bred and excluded the usual Way of other Quadrupeds; yet that which has given Cause to the contrary Opinion is very wonderful, for I have many times seen the young ones just born, fixt and hanging to the Teates of their Dams when they were no bigger than Mice; in this State all their Members were apparent yet not so distinct and perfectly formed but that they looked more like a Foetus than otherwise, and seemed inseparably fixed to the Teats from which no small Force was required to pull their Mouths and then being held to the Teat would not fix to it again. By what Method the Dam after Exclusion fixes them to her Teats is a Secret yet unknown.

The British colonists saw little of value in the opossum. They agreed that it "eats well," but I have failed to find any reference to the opossum as food in periods of near-famine experienced by the colonists. The opossum fur was little esteemed or used.

While the English were making the acquaintance of the opossum in Virginia, French explorers, accompanied by missionaries intent on winning "savage but human souls" for Christ, were wending their way up the St. Lawrence, over the Great Lakes, and thence down the Mississippi to Louisiana, another home of the opossum.

The entering wedge to the opening of the vast northern regions of America was the discovery, in 1497, by John Cabot, of the Banks of Newfoundland with their wealth of fish, the poor man's source of protein food, which had been becoming more and more scarce with the exhaustion of the over-fished waters surrounding Europe. Hence the trek to the Grand Banks. In 1527, John Rut of Bristol, seeking the Strait of Amion, put in at St. John's Harbor, Newfoundland, and saw "eleven saile of Normans, and one Brittaine, and two Portugall Barkes, and all a fishing."

Sailing the Atlantic Ocean from east to west, that is, against the prevailing westerlies of the Temperate Zone, was greatly accelerated by the demonstration by Fletcher of Rye, in 1539, of the art of tacking, or sailing against the wind, with sails trimmed fore and aft. By 1603, six hundred ships could be counted on the Banks, and all French.

This preponderance of French in this region of the world worried Richard Hakluyt. A contemporary of Shakespeare, Hakluyt was secretary to the English Embassy in Paris and, like Trevigliano in Madrid, pried into the commercial activities of nations competing for world trade. Peeved over the sneers aimed at English explorers and discoverers, he started a propaganda campaign to arouse

Dominican opossum. Photograph by Paul Griswald Howes.

the British nation to the importance of colonization. He was "familiarly acquainted with the chiefest Captaines at sea, the greatest Merchants, and the best Mariners of our Nation," like Peter Martyr, the Venetian, in Spain, whose *De Orbe Novo decades* he translated. In addition, Hakluyt collected material for many books of travel, which became historically important enough to be frequently reprinted, even down to the present. Had it not been for Hakluyt, the British might have continued to neglect Canada, in which case this neighbor of ours might today be largely if not wholly French.

In keeping with the spirit of the times, Hakluyt looked upon the "empty" spaces of the world, the lands across the sea, from the viewpoint of exploitation. The question was: How can the newly acquired lands be useful to the Mother Country? Of the new-found world he said in his *Principal Navigations* (1589): "And if the aire be found temperate and the soil yielding wood, water, land and grasse, and the sea fish . . . in divers wayes they may yielde comoditie to England by harbouring and victualling us."

Following the ocean trail for fish, came the land trail for fur. At first the fishermen, trading with the Indians along the shore, bootlegged furs which by royal edict belonged to the king. News of this trade soon spread, so that the enterprising youth of the seventeenth century dreamed of fortunes in beaver fur. As Dryden wrote:

Friend, once 'twas Fame that led thee forth
To brave the Tropick Heat, the Frozen
    North,
Late it was Gold, then Beauty was the spur;
But now our Gallants venture but for fur.

Champlain was the first to open up the St. Lawrence and Great Lakes regions to the *coureur de bois,* the trapper and trader who extracted fortunes for France, if not for himself, from the forests and plains in the form of fur, which for many years meant beaver.

Champlain, however, never reached the

La Salle at the Portage, December 5, 1679. Painting by Arthur Thomas in the courthouse of St. Joseph County, Indiana. Courtesy St. Joseph County Historical Society.

land of the opossum. That privilege was reserved for another Frenchman, René Robert Cavelier, Sieur de la Salle. At the famous Indian portage where canoes going by way of Lake Michigan and the St. Joseph River were transported to the Kankakee, La Salle met his first opossum. Father Hennepin, a member of the party, in 1683 describing La Salle's return to the camp at the portage after an absence over night, says: "He had two animals the size of muskrats hanging at his belt . . . which he had killed with blows of a stick, without these animals taking flight, and which often let themselves hang by the tail from branches of trees and . . . they were very fat." This episode has been memorialized in the painting "La Salle at the Portage," which shows Father Hennepin and other members of the exploring party, including La Salle, who has two opossums hanging from his belt.

With the establishment in 1682 of France's claim to the territory drained by the Mississippi and with the founding of New Orleans in 1718, settlers came, among them amateur naturalists such as Le Page du Pratz and Dumont de Montigny.

Despite the advances made by descriptive zoology and the systematic information available in Linnaeus' *Systema naturae,* which had already passed through several editions, these naturalists from New France, like the pioneers before them, described nature in unscientific terms and in the popular vein. Their writings are of especial interest in that they went a little farther than their predecessors when they added bits of folklore and bizarre theories of their own. The following is a typical example from Du Pratz:

The rat-de-bois' head and tail is like a rat's. He is as big and long as an ordinary cat. His legs are shorter, his paws are long and his toes are armed with claws; his tail almost without hair and made to hook, because when taken by this member he winds himself at once around the finger. His hair is grey and although fine is never smooth. The Indian women spin this and make garters of it which they dye red.

They hunt fowl at night and suck their blood but never eat them. Ordinarily no other animal is seen to walk so slowly, and I took one often walking at my usual pace. When he sees that he is about to be caught his instinct leads him to pretend death, and it is so well carried out that

13

if you were to kill him and cook him he would not move or show any sign of life. It is only when at a great distance, or well hidden, that he starts off to quickly hide in some corner or among some brushwood.

I have always been surprised at the great numbers of this animal seen everywhere, when everything seems to conspire to their destruction, for this animal is of an extraordinary slowness, defenseless, and even though able to climb well, his little ones are born on the ground. It is believed no other animal fights him.—From Arthur's *Furbearers of Louisiana.*

This is a fairly correct characterization of the opossum; De Montigny's description runs about the same but is more fanciful.

The two naturalist-historians just referred to spent many years in Louisiana and had firsthand information. Before them, other Frenchmen had visited the New World and written about the opossum. There was, for example, Father André Thevet, fabricator of tall tales, termed "impudent prevaricator" by the Dutchman De Léry, not without prejudice, for the latter was a Lutheran missionary, Thevet a Catholic, and this was the sixteenth century.

Another explorer who came in contact with the opossum was Father Jean Baptiste du Tertre, whose works are well worth reading, since during his seventeen years' sojourn in the French Antilles he had many experiences of interest to the historian of the seventeenth century. His early work, dated 1654, was so much admired by Charles (César) de Rochefort that the latter lifted much material from it, instead of reporting only what he himself saw on his two trips to the West Indies.

Compared with the French and English explorers, the Dutch contributed little to the story of the opossum, since their attention was focused on the East rather than the West. In the East Indies as merchants they were most successful; they held the Dutch East Indies for over four centuries. In that region they encountered other species of marsupials and gave us descriptions of these nearly a century before the rich marsupial fauna of Australia was revealed to the world.

2

The Cousins Down Under

WITH THE ROUNDING of the Cape of Good Hope by Vasco da Gama in 1497–98 and the establishment of an all-water route to the fabulous Indies, there was ushered in a militant rivalry for the rich Far Eastern trade. Soon after the turn of the century, the Portuguese had established a "factory" in Sumatra and one on Amboina. The Spanish were not far behind, while the Dutch and the English trailed by nearly a century. But when these nations did enter the fray, they fought for the wealth of the East by methods unworthy of enlightened peoples. By the end of the seventeenth century it was fairly well settled that the Spaniards were to be relegated to the Philippines, while the Dutch were to hold the greater part of the East Indies, and the English were to take over India and parts of Borneo and New Guinea. The disposition of New Holland (Australia) was not yet a problem—that land had not yet been discovered.

The existence of an island-continent to the southeast of the Indies had long been suspected but had not been proved. Magellan missed it completely on his famous first circumnavigation of the globe because on that voyage he steered his ship from the strait that bears his name to the northeast in the direction of the Philippines instead of Australia. The Dutchman Tasman reached what is now called Tasmania, but from that point retraced his course instead of rounding the continent. Any contacts with the west coast of Australia were made by ships, mostly Dutch, which were driven out of their course by storms. Without exception the land was described as forbidding, desertlike, devoid of harbors, and inhabited by unfriendly savages. Influenced by these unfavorable reports and discouraged by numerous unprofitable expeditions, the Dutch East India Company lost all interest in New Holland.

Among the ships wrecked on the treacherous Australian coast was the *Batavia*, captained by François Pelsaert, and carrying Dutch emigrants to the factories in the Moluccas. Through this shipwreck the world received from Pelsaert the first description of a member of the kangaroo family. The event occurred in 1629. Pelsaert described his specimen as follows:

We found on these strands large numbers of a species of cat, which are very strange creatures; they are about the size of a hare, the head resembling that of a civet cat; the forepaws are very short, about the length of a finger, on which the animal has five small nails or fingers, resembling those of a monkey's forepaw. Its two hind legs, on the contrary, are upwards of half an ell in length, and it walks on these only, on

15

the flat of the heavy part of the leg, so that it does not run fast. Its tail is very long, like that of a long-legged monkey; if it eats, it sits on its hind legs and clutches its food with its forepaws, just like a squirrel or monkey.

Their manner of generation or procreation is exceedingly strange and highly worth observing. Below the belly the female carries a pouch, into which you may put your hand; inside this pouch are her nipples, and we have found that the young ones grow up in this pouch with the nipples in their mouths. We have seen some young ones lying there, which were only the size of a bean, though at the same time perfectly proportioned, so that it seems certain that they grow there out of the nipples of the mammae, from which they draw their food, until they are grown up and are able to walk. Still they keep creeping into the pouch with them when they are hunted.

Pelsaert's animal has since been identified as the Dama or Tamar wallaby. Troughton states that the Dutchman's description was overlooked for nearly two centuries; in fact, it was unknown to Desmarest, who in 1817 described the species and named it *Thylogale eugenii*. Pelsaert recognized the marsupial character of his strange new beast; but he leaves no hint of acquaintance with earlier descriptions of the opossum, about which a literature had been accumulating. As a well-read and competent Dutch navigator he might be assumed to have had at least a superficial acquaintance with Stade, De Léry, Van Linschoten, and Bleau, fellow-countrymen who had written about the opossum.

Since reading the history of the region inhabited by the rich marsupial fauna "down under," I have often wondered why the Portuguese and the Spaniards, firstcomers to the islands of the Banda and Timor seas, did

Australian wallaby with pouch young, evidently enjoying cake proffered by sailor, W. B. Dickinson, Jr. Courtesy United States Navy.

16

Kangaroo mother with pouch young in Philadelphia Zoo. Photograph by Underwood & Underwood.

not describe these animals, which they must have seen long before Pelsaert. Perhaps someday in Lisbon or in Madrid there will be unearthed manuscripts containing "restricted" material, to use a modern phrase.

Half a century after Pelsaert's ill-fated expedition, the famous British freebooter, explorer, and author William Dampier touched twice on the west coast of New Holland. On his second expedition he landed at Sharks Bay, and there on August 6, 1699, he recorded in his journal that "the Land Animals that we saw were only a Sort of Raccoons different from those of the West-Indies, chiefly as to their legs, for these have very short Forelegs; but go jumping upon them as the others do (and like them are very good meat)." Here "the others" refers to a species seen on his

first voyage to those parts. Not much help from Captain Dampier.

With the arrival at Batavia of the Dutch traveler, author, and painter Cornelis de Bruyn, the East Indian marsupials found a more appreciative observer. De Bruyn illustrated his book, *Travels into Muscovy, Persia, and Part of the East-Indies,* with 320 fine engravings of his attractive paintings. From the 1714 edition I have taken his illustration of the filander, a fit companion piece to that of the kangaroo done by the artist on Captain Cook's first expedition.

Near Batavia, De Bruyn visited the plantation of General Kampanhuizer, who kept in his garden some filanders which had been imported from the Aroe (Aru) Islands, where Alfred Russel Wallace, naturalist of the Malay

17

Filander. From Cornelis de Bruyn's Reizen
*. . . (1714), in the Peabody Library, Balti-
more. This is the earliest picture of an East
Indian marsupial, antedating Cook's kangaroo by about sixty years.*

Archipelago, had his headquarters for a portion of the years 1854–62. There are no marsupials indigenous to Java itself. De Bruyn's
specimen has since been identified by Schre-
ber and named *Macropus brunii;* it is known
by the common name of Aroe wallaby. De
Bruyn described the animal as follows:

When I was at our general's country seat, I saw
a certain animal called filander, which has something very extraordinary about it. There were
several that ran loose with rabbits, and had their
holes under a small hill, encompassed with a
rail. This animal which I have represented in
Plate 213, has its hind legs much longer than its
fore, and has the same skin as a large hare. It has
a head like a fox, and a pointed tail; but what is
most extraordinary in it is, that it has a bag under
its belly; into which the young ones retreat even
when they are very large. One may frequently
see their heads and their necks extended out of
the bag, but when the dam runs, the young are
not visible, but keep in the bottom of the bag,
because she leaps very much in her speed.

Much more entertaining are the facts and
native lore about East Indian marsupials contained in a three-volume work by the Protestant missionary François Valentyn, who
published it in Holland in 1726. There is internal evidence in Valentyn's lengthy accounts of the native animal life that he was
influenced by his earlier reading of works on
the American opossums, particularly the works
of two other Dutchmen, Marcgrave and Piso,
pioneers in Brazilian natural history. Valentyn
does not offer a picture of the filander or the
coescoes because, he says, De Bruyn had already published a drawing.

Another half-century was to pass before the
rumor of the existence of the land mass of
the southern hemisphere was substantiated
by the British navigator Captain James Cook.
In 1768 the Royal Society induced the British
Admiralty to organize an expedition to observe the transit of Venus, calculated to be
most favorably seen from Tahiti, and to undertake further geographical exploration in
the southern seas. Cook was appointed to lead
the expedition, for which mission he was a
"natural," since he was well versed in naviga-
tion and mathematics and had had some experience as an astronomer.

*First printed illustration of the kangaroo.
From Hawkesworth's* Lieutenant Cook's
Voyage round the World *(1773).*

18

Short-eared mountain opossum, Australia. Photograph by Underwood & Underwood.

The expedition was exceedingly well equipped and manned. Sir Joseph Banks headed the scientific staff and had as his assistant Dr. Daniel Charles Solander, a student of the great Linnaeus. In the *Endeavour*, a vessel of 370 tons, the party set out in 1768, returning in 1771 with more world-moving news than had been brought back by any navigator since Columbus.

Having successfully observed the transit of Venus at Tahiti, they sailed west, almost circumnavigated New Zealand, and made history by touching on the east coast of Australia at a point which Cook and his party named Botany Bay. They returned home via Torres Strait, Batavia, and the Cape of Good Hope, thus proving the continental character of Australia.

The preparation of the journal of this voyage was entrusted to the "poet, playwright and miscellaneous writer" John Hawkesworth; Banks later published his own journal. The following extract from Cook's journal, as reported by Hawkesworth, is of especial interest, since it introduces us to the first pictorial representation of the kangaroo.

July 14, 1770. Mr. Gore, who went out this day with his gun, had the good fortune to kill one of the animals which had been so much the subject of speculation: an idea of it will best be conceived by the cut, Plate XX, without which, the most accurate description would answer very little purpose, as it has not similitude enough to any animal already known to admit of illustration by reference. In form it is most like a jerboa, which it also resembles in its motion, as has been observed already, but it differs greatly in size, the jerboa being not larger than a common rat, and this animal, when full grown, as big as a sheep: this animal was a young one, much under full growth, weighing only 28 pounds. The head, neck and shoulders are very small in proportion to the other parts of the body; the tail is nearly as long as the body, thick near the rump and tapering toward the end: the forelegs of this individual were only eight inches long and the hind legs two and twenty: its progress is by successive leaps and jumps.

From this quotation it is obvious that neither Banks nor Solander at first realized that a new type of marsupial animal had been discovered. No doubt Solander had been taught by his professor, Linnaeus, not to classify animals on such superficial analogies as relative size of fore and hind legs. The uncertainty about the identity of the animal was soon dispelled by the discovery of a specimen with a pouch, as the following extract from Banks' journal shows:

Quadrupeds we saw but few and were able to catch but few of those we did see. The largest was called by the natives kangooroo; it is different from any European, and, indeed, any animal I have heard or read of, except the jerboa of Egypt, which is not larger than a rat, while this is larger than a middling lamb. The largest we shot weighed 84 lbs. It may, however, be easily known from all other animals by the singular property of running, or rather hopping, upon only its hinder legs, carrying its forefeet close to its breast. In this manner it hops so fast that in the rocky ground where it is commonly found, it easily beat my greyhound, who, though he was fairly started at several, killed only one and that quite a young one. Another animal was called by the natives je-quoll. . . . The third was of the opossum kind, and much resembled that called by de Buffon *Phalanger.*

Albino alpine opossum (Trichosurus vulpecula), *Australia. Photograph by Underwood & Underwood.*

20

Above: short-headed flying phalanger (Petaurus breviceps), Australia. Below: Queensland gray ring-tailed phalanger (Pseudochirus peregrinus), Australia. Courtesy Zoological Society of London.

Silver-gray or long-eared opossum (Trichosurus vulpecula), *Australia. Courtesy Zoological Society of London.*

July 26, 1770. . . . I had the good fortune to take an animal of the opossum tribe (Didelphis); it was a female, and with it I took two young ones. It was not unlike that remarkable one which de Buffon has described by the name of Phalanger as an American animal. It was, however, not the same. M. de Buffon is certainly wrong in asserting that this tribe is peculiar to America, and in all probability, as Pallas has said in his *Zoologia,* the Phalanger itself is a native of the East Indies, as my animals.

It was Banks who first applied the American Indian word *opossum* to the Australian marsupial. This is more than a coincidence: it serves as a bond between the American and Australian continents with their exclusive possession of marsupial life.

Long before the Dutch and British explorers touched the coast of New Holland, the indigenous tribes of that continent were making their own representations of the kangaroo. The Australian aborigines, considered by some to have the lowest type of human culture, were not devoid of artistic talent. Ten- to fifteen-foot sketches of kangaroos are to be found on rocks and in caves; hunting and fishing scenes are recorded in figures that denote action and are in every way equal to the cave pictures made by Cro-Magnon man in southern France and the Pyrenees. The anthropologist Frederick D. McCarthy, of the Australian Museum at Sydney, has published some examples of aboriginal pictorial compositions which he found in various parts of the island-continent.

It is characteristic of nomadic and hunting peoples, McCarthy points out, to give artistic expression to the habits and postures of the objects of their environment which contribute to their livelihood. So the Australian pictured

22

Cave drawing by Australian aborigines. Sketched by Kurt Dahl, author of In Savage Australia. *By permission of Philip Allan and Company, London.*

flocks of kangaroos and schools of fishes. These paintings and engravings are not merely realizations of a desire for self-expression, but play an important part in the magico-religious rites by which primitive man seeks to attain such control over living animals that he will be assured success in hunting. "Thus art becomes an important medium in their secret and ritual life, and their aesthetic impulse finds inspiration in their economic life."

Having sketched the initial stages in the history of our knowledge of marsupial life, I shall return to the American opossum and shall refer to its Australasian relatives only when they can help us to understand our indigenous species. But first a short background chapter about our credulous ancestors of western Europe, athirst for news, the more sensational and extravagant, the more welcome.

3

The Su and the Age of Credulity

BEFORE proceeding to weave together fact and fiction concerning marsupial life, let us take a glance at the naïveté and credulity of the age in which the most novel of all animals appeared upon the scene.

The fourteenth, fifteenth, and sixteenth centuries have been called the Age of Credulity, but this period was also the age of the revival of learning and the rediscovery of Greek and Roman literature, prompting a renewal of interest in ancient natural history, "the plausible but false as well as the astonishing but true." The most popular author of the day, Pliny the Elder, unlike the thoroughly scientific Aristotle, was quite uncritical. To him fact and fiction were all the same; he recorded nature lore where he found it and gathered together the animal and plant anecdotes and legends of the day and presented them with all the assurance of fact. In his world-famous *Natural History* Pliny included winged horses, unicorns, and other legendary creatures. Imaginary horrors on land and sea were giants, satyrs, dragons, and chimaeras; the gorgon, the griffin, and the phoenix—all destructive of human life and not to be withstood by any man. Take the gorgon, for example, as related by Topsell (1607), science popularizer of his day:

Among the manifold and divers sorts of Beasts which are bred in Affricke, it is thought that the *Gorgon* is brought forth in that countrey. It is a fearful and terrible beast to behold: It hath high and thicke eie-lids, eies not very great, but much like Oxes or Bugils, but all fiery and bloudy, which neyther looke directly forwarde, nor yet upwards, but continuallye downe to the earth, and therefore are called in Greeke *Catobleponta*. From the crowne of their head downe to their nose, they have a long hanging mane, which makes them look fearefully. It eateth deadly and poysonfull hearbs, and if at any time he see a Bull, or other creature whereof he is afraid, he presently causeth his mane to stand upright, and, being so lifted up, opening his lips, and gaping wide, sendeth forth of his throat a certaine sharpe and horrible breath, which infecteth, and poysoneth the air above his head, so that all living creatures which draw the breath of that aire are grievously afflicted thereby, loosing both voyce and sight, they fall into leathall and deadly convulsions. It is bred in Hesperis and Libia.

In the ocean, sea serpents existed everywhere and were pictured on world maps for more than decorative reasons. So great a man as Ambroise Paré, who in the sixteenth century was able to revolutionize obstetrical practice as well as surgery of the battlefield, believed in mermaids and mermen.

Danger from imaginary monsters in the

24

sea was as much feared as the treachery of the elements. No wonder, then, that Columbus had great difficulty recruiting sailors for the *Santa María*, the *Niña*, and the *Pinta*. He recalled how, in 1484, sailing under the aegis of Henry the Navigator, he had been forced to turn back from the Azores because fear overtook the sailors.

To add to the worries of sailing masters, Marco Polo in 1295 had brought back from the kingdom of the Great Khan the Mongolian legend of the great roc, or rukh, a story that was confirmed by no less a person than Jordanus, Bishop of India under Pope John XXII and a man of undoubted honor and veracity. The story would, however, have reached European readers later anyway with the popularization of the *Arabian Nights* tales. The roc, it was averred, was so big that it could easily lift an elephant into the air. It had a wingspread of sixteen paces and feathers a length of nine paces.

The Grand Khan . . . sent messengers to the island . . . to examine the truth of the wonderful things told of it. When they returned to the presence of His Majesty they brought with them ["as I have read," said Marco Polo] a feather of the Rukh, positively affirmed to have measured nine paces. This surprising exhibition afforded His Majesty extreme pleasure, and upon those by whom it was presented he bestowed valuable gifts.

This tale was believed by many; but as for Marco Polo's statement that in China "rocks" (coal) were burned as fuel—that was considered impossible.

On the theory that every imaginary monster has a factual prototype, one may philosophize a bit on the story of the roc. There seems little doubt that the Arabs and the Egyptians had from ancient times visited Madagascar and had seen on that island the giant super-ostrich, the Aepyornis, which became extinct so recently that some of its eggs have been recovered from the vegetation of the marshes, and these, as well as skeletons of the giant bird, are today to be found in mu-

seums. Whereas the ostrich egg is equivalent to twenty-five hens' eggs, the Aepyornis egg has a volume of eight ostrich eggs.

On such a factual foundation a good story could be built by enlarging the Aepyornis sufficiently and endowing it with correspondingly powerful wings, for the Madagascar bird was not a flier, but a runner, like the ostrich, and hence had only rudimentary wings.

Among the originators of strange beasts supposed to inhabit the New World, perhaps

The "su," figment of the fertile imagination of Father André Thevet. Above: from Thevet (1558). Below: from Forer's German edition of Gesner (1563).

25

the most imaginative was Father André Thevet, inventor of the fabulous "su." This audaciously conceived creature is described in his book *Les singularitez de la France antarctique* (1557), the 1568 English version of which had the following title, all-inclusive, in keeping with the custom of the day: *The New Found Worlde, or Antarctike, wherein is contained wõderful and strange things, as well of humaine creatures, as Beastes, Fishes, Foules, and Serpents, Trees, Plants, Mines of Golde and Silver: garnished with many learned aucthorities, travailed and written in the French tong, by that excellent learned man, Master Andrewe Thevet. And now newly translated into Englishe, wherein is reformed the errours of the auncient Cosmographers.*

Thevet's work did not escape the notice of English authors. His material and that of others were taken over by Edward Topsell, a clergyman who "had a living at Sayresham" and who wrote books "to passe away the Sabbaoths in heavenly meditation upon earthly creatures." He compiled one volume with these details on the title page: *The History of four-footed Beasts and Serpents describing their true and lively Figure, their several Names, Conditions, Kinds, Virtues (both Natural and Medicinal), Countries of their Breed, their Love and Hatred of Mankind, and the wonderful work of God in their Creation, Preservation and Destruction. Interwoven with curious Variety of Historical Narratives out of Scriptures, Fathers, Philosophers, Physicians and Poets. Illustrated with divers Hieropgyphicks and Emblems &c both pleasant and profitable for Students in All Faculties and Professors. Collected out of the Writings of Conradus Gesner and other authors, by Edward Topsel, 1658. Revised by J. R. MD.*

How is this for a blurb? Every author his own salesman!

The following is Topsell's version of Thevet's su:

There is a Region in the New-found World, called *Gigantes,* and the Inhabitants thereof are called Patagones; now because their Countrey is cold, being far in the South, they clothe themselves with the skins of a Beast called in their own tongue *Su,* for the reason that the Beast liveth for the most part near the water, therefore call it by the name of *Su,* which signifieth water. The true Image thereof as it was taken by *Thevetus,* I have inserted, for it is of a very deformed shape, and monstrous presence, a great ravener and untamable wilde Beast. When Hunters that desire her skin set upon her, she flyeth very swift, carrying her young ones upon her back, and covering them with her broad tail: now forasmuch no Dog or Man dareth to approach neer unto her (because such is the wrath thereof, that in the pursuit she killeth all that cometh neer her): the Hunters dig several pits or great holes in the Earth, which they cover with boughs, sticks, and earth, so weakly that if the Beast chance at any time to come upon it, she and her young ones fall down into the pit and are taken.

This cruel, untamable, impatient, violent ravening and bloudy Beast, perceiving that her natural strength cannot deliver her from the wit and policy of man, her hunters, (for being inclosed, she can never get out again), the Hunters being at hand to watch her downfall, and work her overthrow, first of all to save her young ones from taking and taming, she destroyeth all with her own teeth; for there was never any of them taken alive; and when she seeth the Hunters come about her, she roareth, cryeth, howleth, brayeth, and uttereth such a fearful, noysome, and terrible clamour, that the men which watch to kill her, are not thereby little amazed, but at last being animated, because there can be no resistance, they approach, and with their darts and spears wound her to death, and then take off her skin, and leave the carcass in the earth. And that is all I finde recorded of this most savage Beast.

Although this creature was once identified as the opossum, this interpretation must be rejected and the su regarded as a pure fabrication of Thevet. Gesner included the su in his zoology but said he had no choice but to do so "on the authority of Thevet." In Forer's German translation of Gesner (who wrote in Latin) is found this short treatment of the su:

Concerning the vilest animal ever seen, called Su in the new lands: There is a place in the new-found land which the inhabitants call Patagones, and since the place is very cold they clothe themselves with the pelt of an animal which they call Su, that is, water, because of the fact that it lives mostly near the water. It is very rapacious, vile; as the figure proves it takes its young on its back, covers them with its long tail, flees, is caught in pits and killed with arrows.

The reader will certainly agree with Gesner that, judging from the pictures here reproduced, one would not like to meet such a creature. This beast also appears in the historic and artistic copper engraving by the elder De Bry, who included in his Brazilian landscape both the authentic opossum and Thevet's su (p. 132). The reader will appreciate having a whole South American zoo in one picture: crocodiles, boa constrictors, iguanas, a scorpion of heroic size, the armadillo, and jaguars; in the background a river and plenty of active volcanoes that do not seem to worry several human beings shown near their habitations.

While Aldrovandi, in his famous seventeenth-century zoology, repudiates the su, he does picture an egg containing a human head with hair of serpents; likewise he accepts, "on the authority of Lycosthenes," the woman who lays and incubates eggs from which emerge giants.

To exploit the credulous and uncritical Topsell a bit more, I quote his exaggerated account of the American skunk. The European readers must by comparison have felt very well satisfied with their own *Stinkkatze:*

The Biaratica is of the bignesse of a Cat, like a Ferret it hath a white stroake and a gray along the backe, like a cross, very well made; it feeds upon birds and their egges, and upon other things, especially Ambar, and loveth it so well, that all the night he goeth by the Seaside to seeke it, and where there is any, he is the first. It is greatly feared, not because it hath any teeth, or any other defensive thing, but it hath a certaine ventositie so strong and so evill of sent, that it doth penetrate the wood, the stones, and all that it encountereth withall, and it is such, that some Indians have died of the stench. And the dog that cometh near it escapeth not: and this smell lasteth fifteen, twentie, or more dayes; and it is such, that if it lighteth near some towne, it is perfectly disinhabited. And that they may not be perceived, they scrape a hole in the grund, and there within they voide that ventositie, and cover it with earth; and when they are found, that they may not bee taken, their defense is to cast out that stench.

Although De Léry criticized Thevet and gave him the sobriquet of "mendacious liar," he himself was somewhat prone to exaggeration; for in connection with the not inconsiderable digging ability of armadillos, he relates that they will "dig so fast, that several men with mattocks have not been able to do so much as one of these with his snout alone, so that they presently convey themselves to a sure refuge underground." We may let that stand as rather mild in view of the hyperbolic performance of other authors. Besides, I have myself seen the armadillo practically sink into the sand when pursued by dogs. However, De Léry could not have examined the armadillo carefully or he would not have overlooked the powerful claws with which it does the digging.

Peter Martyr was another writer who passed on to posterity incredible tales, gleaned from the yarns of returning travelers. In a very ancient type of story, animals are endowed with human intelligence. This, coupled with their superior strength, as in the case of Moby Dick, enables them to combat man. So the matu (manatee) in Peter Martyr's Third Decade is "a tame fish that comes to the edge of the stream or lake in answer to call and ferries men across on its back—except Christians, since a young man of that faith had once thrown a sharp dart into its skin."

The interested reader will find in Ashton's *Curious Creatures in Zoology* an excellent account of strange beasts and in Robin's collection *Animal Lore in English Literature*

27

many examples of literary allusion to animal legends. Even so serious a writer as Oliver Goldsmith apparently accepted as true certain animal legends in his *History of the Earth and Animated Nature,* published just after his death (1774). Our attention has been called to these exaggerations by John Wesley, author of the competing *Compendium of Natural Philosophy.* Commenting on Goldsmith's work, Wesley wrote the following entry in his Diary, March 25, 1775: "Many times he exposes credulity of other writers, but falls for Bishop Pontopedan's cracken *[Kraken],* and sea serpent, the one a mile across, the other raising himself higher than the mainmast of a man-of-war."

Before leaving the realm of pure legend and traditional beliefs and returning to more scientific aspects (which it is high time I were doing), I close this chapter by citing an advertisement from the *Boston Gazette* (1763):

CATAMOUNT

TAIL LIKE A LYON, LEGS LIKE A BEAR'S, CLAWS LIKE AN EAGLE, EYES LIKE A TIGER, COUNTENANCE A MIXTURE OF EVERYTHING FIERCE AND SAVAGE. HE IS EXCEEDINGLY RAVENOUS AND DEVOURS ALL SORTS OF CREATURES HE CAN COME UPON. WHOEVER INCLINES TO SEE THIS CREATURE MAY COME TO THE PLACE AFORESAID PAYING A SHILLING EACH AND SHALL BE WELCOME FOR THEIR MONEY.

4

The Opossum Gets a Name

THE FIRST MARSUPIAL which the western Europeans encountered came upon the scene quite nameless. Pinzón, who brought the foundling to Spain in 1500, so far as we know furnished no name; nor did Peter Martyr, to whom Pinzón communicated, probably in personal interview, the first offhand description of the strangest of all beasts. If Pinzón had lingered among the Indians in the land of the opossum, he might have heard the native name, rendered it *simile sonans* into written vowels and consonants, and made a name that would be current today. Dozens of animals and plant names have come down to us in that way. Take the words for the big cats of the Americas: the Tupi Indian *jaguâra* gave us *jaguar;* the Guarini *cuguacuara, cougar,* according to Marcgrave. *Puma* is Peruvian (Quechuan); but when you use the transplanted *panther* you are talking pure Greek. The missionary Valentyn asked his East Indian charges their name for a certain marsupial; he thought he heard *filandoe,* and, being a good Greek scholar, he put the name down as *philander* ("lover of mankind") and *philander* or *filander* it is today.

In the same way, Captain James Cook and Sir Joseph Banks thought they heard the natives say *kangooroo,* which they duly recorded in their several books; hence *kangaroo,* in its various spellings, is the word by which a certain kind of Australian animal is known throughout the world—and this in spite of the fact that no native word sounding anything like that has since been heard in Queensland! Perhaps a native cleared his throat at the psychological moment and the white visitors had the word *kangaroo.*

The first name for the opossum to be printed in books was invented by Gesner in 1558. One would think that, since the pouch was the sensational feature of the new discovery, the name would have been based on that character, as indeed it was later: Marsupialia, from the Latin *marsupium,* "pouch." But Gesner, reading Peter Martyr's original 1516 description—"half monkey, half fox"—came up with *simivulpa* or *simia vulpina,* "fox-monkey" in English, *Fuchsaffe* in German. Aldrovandi, "the Italian Gesner," also used *simivulpa* as well as *vulpisimia;* but by 1637 he had gathered a number of additional names from books of travel published after Gesner.

Before trailing the explorers through South and Central America to discover where they picked up the various synonyms, of which there were scores, let us backtrack a bit to the ancient Mayans and Aztecs. Among the latter the name was *tlaquatzin,* made known through Hernández and others who lived in

Mexico after Cortez. *Tlacuache* is the common Mexican name today; Clavijero spells it *tlacuatzin*. Gadow in his travels through southern Mexico heard natives use *ratón tlacuache*.

The Mayans made much of the opossum, their *och*. Other mammals were designated by compounds of *och*: as, for example, *pay-och*, one kind of skunk, and *kex-pach-och*, a porcupine.

In various parts of South America the early travelers heard the natives use sundry names for the opossum, some of which would seem to be cognate and therefore to have come from a common stem. I have, however, not gone into the philology of this matter but have merely recorded what I have found in the many books of travel which I have consulted over the years.

Let us consider first some names that originated in the valley of the Amazon. Stade, returning in 1555 at the end of seven years of captivity among the Indians, brought back the Indian name which he spelled *serway* or *serwoy*. Marcgrave and Piso, according to their literary executor De Laet, called the animal *carigua* or *sarigoi*, and later authors modified this root with considerable freedom. The Italian Maffeius used *cerigoni*, but let *cerigon* and even *cerigo* pass also; Nierembergius Latinized the name to *cerigonum*. Inasmuch as the Spanish and the Portuguese *c* and *s* are practically equivalent, we have *sarigoi, sarigueya, sarigua,* and other endings until the great "authority" Georges Louis Leclerc, Comte de Buffon—Buffon for short—settled this little matter as he did weightier ones, Gallicizing the name to *sarigue*. This name long rivaled *opossum* in world literature and might still predominate if the French had won the Seven Years' War, of which the French and Indian Wars were the American echo. For one breach of philological ethics, however, one can hardly forgive the Baron, for he took *carigueia* and combined it with Marcgrave's *tai-ibi* (both meaning "opos-

sum") into *carigueibeju,* and zoological nomenclature had reached its all-time low.

The much traveled and prolific writer Gonzalo Fernández de Oviedo y Valdés (1555) found *churcha* used in parts of South America; in Cuba it was *zurcan*. In the same century Pedro de Creza de León heard the word *churcha* in Peru. He wrote:

An animal like a small fox, with a long tail and short feet, of gray color and the head of a fox. I once saw one of these creatures which had seven young ones near it. Directly it was frightened, or heard a noise, it opened its bag which nature had placed on its belly, put its young inside, and fled so swiftly that I was astonished at its agility, being so small and running so rapidly with such a weight. They call this creature *churcha.*

Churcha on the Atlantic coast; *churcha* also on the Pacific. In Clavijero's *History of Mexico* one finds *chincha*.

While the Dutch had their capital at Mauritius on the island of Antonio Vas (1630–54) and after they retired under Portuguese pressure to Dutch New Guinea, they knew the opossum as the *Boschrot* or *Boschratze*, meaning "bushrat," which corresponds to the *rat de bois*, "rat of the woods," the name which the French applied to the opossum of Louisiana. But Madame Maria Merian, daintily painting the gorgeous Guiana butterflies from 1699 to 1701, preferred the more elegant *rat de forêt*. In nearby French Guiana, the Cayenne city folk dismissed the opossum with the appellation *pia* or *puant*, "the fetid one."

In the region of the Río de la Plata, Azara's opossum is abundant. It is known as the *comedreya*, meaning "weasel," but *micuré* is also applied to it, which in the language of the Guarani Indians (Argentine) means "stinker." However, Rengger, who was living in Paraguay over a century ago, gave the meaning of *micuré* as "little pig," saying the animal was so called "probably because of the odor it emits; but this is the only similarity with the wild pig of Paraguay." In Brazil today

Portrait of the Virginia opossum, the woapink *or "white-face" of the Lenape Indians. Courtesy Edmond J. Farris, Wistar Institute of Anatomy and Biology, Philadelphia.*

gambá is the common name for the local opossum and is the dictionary equivalent of *opossum* and *sarigueya.*

In Ecuador, Padre Gumilla picked up a great deal of natural history, and he treated the opossum more fully than either Belt or Bates a century later. To quote from the French edition of 1753: "The Indians also hunt the *faras*, which they call also *revales*, because of its destructiveness to bananas, papayas, and other fruits which are cultivated, not for food because of the unappetizing odor of the flesh."

Central American Spaniards were more practical, simply transferring the Spanish name *zorro*, "fox," to the opossum "because of its fondness for chickens and its stealth and cunning." A name sometimes used is *zorro pelón*, which has reference to the hair-

lessness of the tail. *Raposa* or *rapoza*, "female fox," occurs in the literature, and it was already known to John Ray in 1693. Indians call the ordinary opossum *guica* or *quica*, the water opossum *quica de agua*. I have also run across the designation *juron* (pronounced hooron) used by San Salvadorans.

Of greater interest to us in the United States is the Indian origin of *opossum*, now of world-wide acceptance.

In Choctaw the opossum was called *shukata* or *shookhuta;* in Tuscarora, *cheera;* in Cherokee, *seegua;* in Lenape, *woapink*, meaning "white-face," according to Benjamin Smith Barton, successively professor of natural history, botany, and materia medica at the University of Pennsylvania, also ethnologist and friend of the Indians, especially of the neighboring Lenapes. Although Dr. Barton well

31

knew the *Systema naturae* of Linnaeus, he ignored the official *Didelphis virginiana*, preferring the Lenape-derived *woapink*.

Opossum, too, is an Indian name; the *-um* is not the Latin neuter singular, although Charles de Kay, author of the *Natural History of New York*, did think the name came from the Latin. This recalls a bit of pleasantry on the part of the scholarly George W. Corner: "The opossum should offer you an opportunity for analysis along the lines you suggest. Strength to your arm—and let our motto be (in the noble tongue of Julius Caesar): '*Possumus*.'"

The name opossum originated with Captain John Smith, leader of the Jamestown Colony. Writing much later, John Brickell, M.D., the King's surveyor in Carolina, tells us that the word actually was *possum*, but that this was preceded by a grunt, hence the *o—opossum*.

The spelling varied for many decades. Some samples may be cited. The list will amuse our school youth, perpetually accused of being poor spellers.

opassom—Captain John Smith, *A Map of Virginia* (1612)

opassam—Harris, quoting John Smith (also *New English Dictionary*)

ouassom—*Purchas His Pilgrimes* (1616), also quoting Smith

opussum—Strachey (1610–12), in Virginia

apossumes—Ralph Hamor (1615), in Virginia

ospason—Du Tertre (1654)

opuson—John Clayton (1688), in Virginia

oppassum—Klein, *Quadrupedum* (1751)

apossum—Oliver Goldsmith, *Animated Nature* (1774)

opossum—English edition of Clavijero (1787)

Webster's New International Dictionary says that *opossum* is of Algonquian origin, coming from Virginian *apasum*, "white animal," and Ojibway *wabassim*. (Lenape and Delaware belong to the same language group.)

The American Indian name *opossum* was,

however, not destined to remain exclusively on this continent. Recognizing the general relationship of certain Australian marsupials to the American opossum, Captain James Cook and Sir Joseph Banks dubbed them *opossums* also: "Besides the animals which I have before mentioned," Cook writes, "called by the natives kangaroo or kanguru, here are Wolves [dingoes], Possums, an animal like a rat. . . ." And again on his third voyage, he saw an animal on Van Diemen's Land (Tasmania) which he called opossum: "The only animal of the quadruped kind we got was a sort of opossum, about twice the size of a large rat and is, most probably, the male of that species, found at Endeavour River, as mentioned in Hawkesworth's collection of voyages."

Captain John Hunter, in his *Historical Journal* (1793), fixes the name opossum on animals in New South Wales, as the following quotation shows:

The opossum is also numerous here, but it is not exactly like the American opossum; it partakes a good deal of the kangaroo in the strength of its tail and make of its forefeet. . . . There are several other animals of a smaller size, down as low as the field rat which in some part or other partakes of the kangaroo and opossum: we have caught many rats with this pouch for carrying their young when pursued, and the legs, claws, and tail of this rat are exactly like the kangaroo.

So it came about that the word opossum was used for certain kinds of Australian marsupials, and the name has stuck and is now ineradicably embedded in the parlance of the region.

The naturalist Ellis Troughton, in his *Furred Animals of Australia*, suggests that we continue to use *opossum* to cover the American species, leaving *possum*, without the *o*, to apply to the phalangers, a family native to Australia. Fair enough, but let's not reduce such an agreement to a signed and sealed treaty, for someone among us might make a slip and accidentally say "possum" for short, just as we say "squash" for the Indian *mus-quash*, or "coon" for "raccoon." We must keep causes for international friction down to a minimum.

This bewildering multiplicity of names in the vernacular was already deplored in 1826 by a veteran traveler in South America, Maximilian, Prinz zu Wied-Neuwied. The difficulty still exists, for according to the *Encyclopaedia Britannica* there are 136 English names for the Atlantic salmon.

So much for the local designations applied to the pouch-bearing mammal of the Western Hemisphere—names which, as Roy Bedichek says in *Adventures of a Texas Naturalist*, "you can use in flesh-and-blood conversation." He recognized, however, that there must be terms internationally understood, to him "those fearsome, cumbrous names duly frozen in print for the great convenience of scientists scattered over the world." In the course of time, scientists did solve the problem of making order out of the chaos of names of animals and plants.

We may begin this story with the seventeenth-century zoologist John Ray, often called the Father of English Natural History. While the pioneer zoologists Gesner and Aldrovandi brought together animal lore from hard-to-get books, it was John Ray who first attempted to arrange plants and animals according to a system based on certain structures. In the case of mammals, for example, form, number, and arrangement of teeth and of digits constitute important characters on which systems of classification are based. From this pioneer classifier on, all systems have been based on readily determined points of structure and measurements thereof, and more lately on physiological and biochemical characters also.

Any system, to be a success, must have but one name for any one kind of animal. Moreover, the system must be able to take care of the thousands and hundreds of thousands of species to be discovered in the future. The descriptions must be so accurate that anyone who examines a specimen of a given species can with certainty identify it by means of the published data. The reader will see at once that this implies international agreement among scientists. Such agreement has, indeed, been realized.

The system which made such an ideal possible was the work of the Swedish Carl von Linné, better known as Linnaeus. The system was worked up in a series of editions of his *Systema naturae,* of which the first appeared in 1735. The tenth edition contains the well-matured, workable, and now accepted "Linnaean system," according to which each animal and plant is given a twofold name, the genus name and the species name. A species differs from all others, while a genus is a collection of species that have some important character in common. The genus name is conventionally spelled with a capital, the species name always with a small initial, even when taken from a proper name. For example, when obeying Proverbs 6:6—"Go to the ant, thou sluggard; consider her ways, and be wise"—I discovered a new ant species which I sent, with notes on habits, to William Morton Wheeler. This he named *Atta (Mycetosoritis) hartmanni* Wheeler n. sp. 1907. I am also immortalized in a subspecies: *Trachymyrmex turrifex* Wheeler *caroli* n. subsp. Wheeler. These ants raise fungus gardens on caterpillar dung. I might add that when John Henry Comstock, Cornell entomologist, discovered a new genus of louse on a bat from a Texas cave into which I had guided him some forty years ago, he expressed his intention of naming this louse after me; but I believe that I escaped this questionable distinction.

Genera are gathered together into the next higher group, the family, families into orders, and orders into classes.

The few marsupials that Linnaeus knew he classed with the Ferae, which included, among others, dogs, cats, bears, and moles. Pennant placed opossums among the Carnivora (nearly the same as Ferae), while Cuvier in 1817 put them at the end of the Carnivora. But in the 1829 edition of Cuvier's work the Marsupialia, now grown greatly in number of species, were elevated to a separate order. This step was fully justified, for marsupials have certain identifying characters, entirely aside from the possession of the pouch, which, by the way, many marsupials lack. All marsupials have a pair of distinctive bones, called "marsupial bones," attached to the pelvis; the posterior angle of the lower jawbone is bent inward; the brain is very primitive, having only rudimentary cerebral lobes; there are two separate uteri, and the eggs, though tiny, are surrounded by egg white and a shell membrane, as in lizard eggs; and finally the young are born extremely immature. These are some of the reasons why marsupials are entitled to a separate order.

Linnaeus at first distinguished three species of marsupials; Pennant, fifteen species; the Argentine authors Cabrera and Yepes count ninety, eighty of which they assign to South America; our own Gerrit S. Miller, Jr., lists twelve species of Didelphis, fifteen of Marmosa, six of Philander, two of Metachirops, one of Metachirus, one of Monodelphis, and one of Chironectes—all opossums—in North America.

Now it happens that Linnaeus misspelled the generic name which he gave to the opossum, Didelphis, substituting an *i* for the *y* which should be there if the Greek derivation had been accurately followed (*di-*, "two"; *delphys*, "uterus"). But according to the established rule of the International Commission on Zoological Nomenclature the name must stand as Linnaeus wrote it, since he created the name and gave the first description of the genus.

Finally, let us inquire what the correct technical name for the Virginia opossum actually is and why.

Pennant (1790) was the first to differentiate the United States opossum from others,

Left hind foot of juvenile opossum, with opposable clawless "thumb." It was this handlike foot which prompted the discoverer of the opossum, Pinzón, in 1500 to describe the animal as "part monkey."

and George Shaw (1800) also described it, but their descriptions were considered too meager for certain identification. Both descriptions were therefore rejected in favor of that of Robert Kerr (1792), whose book is entitled: *The Animal Kingdom or Zoological System of the Celebrated Sir Charles Linnaeus: Class I, Mammalia, Being a Translation of That Part of the* Systema Naturae *as Lately Published, with Great Improvement by Professor Gmelin of Göttingen, together with Numerous Additions from More Recent Zoological Writers and Illustrated with Copper Plates.*

The following is the classical description which stood the test of adequacy:

From the top of the nose to the tail this animal is 20 inches long, and the tail twelve; the nose is long and sharp pointed, having long, stiff hairs on each side; the ears are large, rounded, naked, very thin, of a black colour, and edged with white; the eyes are small, black, lively, and surrounded with a dusky space; the face is covered with soft, short, white hair; the neck is short, thick and of

34

a dirty yellow colour at the sides; the hind part of the neck, and the back, are covered with long, soft, uneven hairs, which are yellowish-white at the bottom, blackish in the middle, and whitish at the ends; the hair at the sides is of the same length, mixed with dirty white and dusky colours; the belly is covered with soft, wooly, dirty white hairs; the feet are dusky, with white claws, having five toes each; the great toes on the hind feet are distinct, and like a thumb; the base of the tail is hairy; the rest is prehensile, and covered with small scales, like a snake, the first half being black, the rest white; the body is round, very thick and clumsy, with short black legs; the female has a pouch or false belly in which the teats are placed, and in which the young take shelter immediately after birth, fastening so closely to the teats that they can scarcely be separated; they are very small, naked, blind and resemble foetuses; when older they acquire hair, get their sight, and venture out of the pouch but to return at the least alarm. This animal is very fetid; but the flesh, even of the old ones, is very good and eats like that of a sucking pig.

This is the description that determined the official scientific name of the Virginia opossum, which is and ever will be *Didelphis virginiana* Kerr.

In giving the geographical distribution of this species, Kerr was wrong. He said it "inhabits Virginia, Louisiana, Mexico, Brazil and Peru." As a matter of fact, the range stops on this side of the Rio Grande, beyond which one finds *D. marsupialis* and others. Kerr could not, of course, judge the range from the opossum skins he studied in the Leveran Museum —all of which goes to show that knowledge grows by slow accretions, one point at a time being established, each generation correcting the mistakes of the preceding and adding its own new truths, and errors. Such is the expansion of our cultural inheritance, which, since the perfection of the art of printing, has grown at an accelerated tempo. With newer and faster means of communication, knowledge—if not wisdom with it—may be expected from now on to mushroom and quickly overflow into still dark continents.

A close-up of a Virginia opossum (enlarged). Photograph by Lambert Martin—FPG.

5

What Manner of Beast Is This?

THE EARLIEST DESCRIPTIONS of the opossum were couched in terms of animals which the reporters knew at home, in western Europe. "A muzzle like a fox, a tail like a monkey, ears like a bat, and human hands similar to those of monkeys," wrote Peter Martyr. We have already noted Captain John Smith's words in characterizing the Virginia opossum, largest of all American species: "An Opassum hath an head like a Swine, and a taile like a Rat, and is of the bignes of a Cat."

Size, of course, is an accident of minor significance in the classification of animals; but the early explorers, even the early zoologists, little realized this. Opossums vary greatly in size, some being no larger than small rats, yet these, too, are members of the family.

Let us examine some of the characteristics of the opossum for better acquaintance with this type of animal.

Comparing the opossum with the fox is an insult to that shrewd animal whose instinctive wisdom has made it the prototype of human cunning. By contrast, the opossum is perhaps the stupidest of all mammals. We read in Brehm's *Tierleben:*

The opossum is plentiful and cheap in the animal market. But it is a dumb, dull pet, for its activity affords the owner little pleasure. I have seen none of that intelligence ascribed to it by Audubon. It is sluggish, lazy, sleepy, and forbiddingly stupid, at least in captivity.

The naturalist John Burroughs on one occasion found an opossum under his cabin and made friends with it, but his only reward, he relates, was that the animal simply "opened his mouth and grinned up at me in a sort of comical, idiotic way."

The nocturnal habits of the animal make it sluggish and unresponsive in the daytime when one is able to enjoy a pet; yet even in its liveliest hours, I can testify, it has little to recommend it. Troughton makes the same unflattering remarks about the Australian marsupials.

Rengger was the first to relate the moronic behavior of the opossum to the volume of its brain, which is small when compared with that of better-known and more popular animals of similar size:

All three genera of opossum which I met in Paraguay may be tamed to a certain extent; i.e., they become so far accustomed to persons that one may touch them without being bitten; but they never learn to recognize their caretaker and in fact show not the slightest intelligence, which is just what one may expect from their relatively small brain box and a facial angle of seventeen degrees or less. But nobody in Paraguay would think of making a pet of an opossum, for its ugliness and odor are repellent.

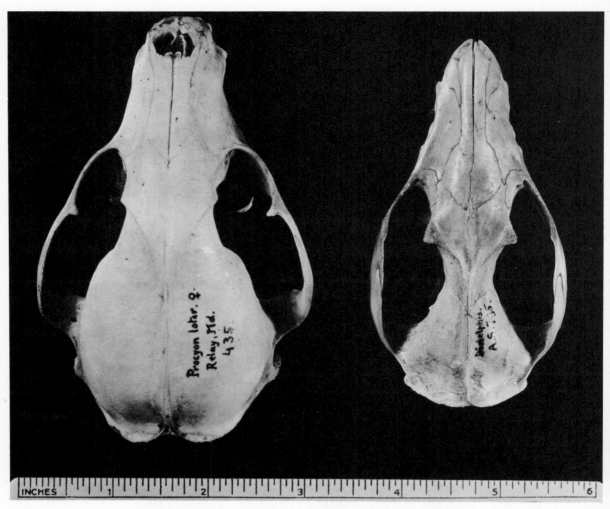

Skulls of raccoon (left) and opossum, showing relative size of brain cases. Photograph by Vernon Bailey. Courtesy Nature Magazine.

About a century after Rengger had thus brought the opossum into disrepute as a pet, Vernon Bailey, genial naturalist of the United States Biological Survey, measured the brain box or cranial capacity of a number of animals and in this way gave striking demonstration of the meager brain substance possessed by the subject of this book. The relative capacities were measured in terms of the number of beans required to fill the brain case. The result is shown in the following table:

Opossum	21	Porcupine	70
Skunk I	35	Red fox	198
Skunk II	50	Coyote	325
Arctic hare	46	Gray wolf	438

An interesting comparison is that between the sprightly and companionable raccoon, a universal favorite, and the opossum, which nobody loves. Bailey's illustration of the skulls of these two mammals that occupy similar habitats in America is reproduced in the accompanying figure. The skulls shown are of approximately the same size, but what a difference in the part that harbors the brain! No phrenologist is needed to interpret the sizable bumps of smartness on the skull of

38

the raccoon, their absence on that of the opossum.

What part of the brain did nature deny the opossum? Offhand one would say the part that has to do with "intelligence." In wild animals, intelligence might be defined as ability to avoid danger, to find food, and to solve the immediate and pressing problems of living. In the long run, a species with a superior brain is the one more likely to survive changing conditions of climate and habitat. In captivity, the ability to learn would be a criterion of intelligence. While it is true that the opossum has survived in competition with the so-called "higher" mammals, its fecundity has had more to do with that than has its intelligence. However that may be, certain it is that the opossum is woefully defective in frontal brain lobes, with which intelligence is usually associated. The raccoon has so much of this kind of gray matter that the halves are connected by a thick band of nerve fibers. The opossum has no such band and doesn't need it, for there are too few brain cells to require many connecting fibers. But the opossum's center for the sense of smell is as well developed as that of other mammals, and those nerve centers that regulate breathing, heartbeat, blood pressure, and other vital functions are fully developed. Since these lower centers are present also in reptiles and birds, their possession is no especial compliment to the opossum.

What has been said about the low grade of the opossum's intelligence holds also for its marsupial cousins: stupidity runs in the family. This branch of the animal kingdom stood still in the process of evolution, outstripped by its competitors, the higher mammals.

The eyes of the opossum are black and prominent, "somewhat exophthalmic," i.e. popeyed, "reminding one of round glass beads set into a stuffed specimen by a taxidermist," according to Krieg. "Shoe-button eyes" Miss Shanafelt called those of her mouse opossums.

The jet-blackness of the eyeballs is due to the fact that the eye is all pupil, for the iris does not come into view at all, except in the brightest light, which the animal shuns. Perhaps the wide-open pupil is an adaptation to the opossum's crepuscular and nocturnal habits. But the opossum's vision is never very keen even in the daytime, if one is to judge by its utter lack of response to objects passed before it.

An outstanding character of the opossum, more particularly of Central and South American species, is the black streak which surrounds the eye and tapers to a point on the cheek or the snout. In general, the opossum's face is white, hence the Lenape and Delaware Indian name *woapink*, "white-face"; *Webster's New International Dictionary* translates *opossum* "white animal." The white face renders the black eye streak the more prominent, as various pictures in this book will show. It is the eyespot which helps us to identify this animal in the much conventionalized drawings of the Mayans.

The opossum responds poorly to visual stimuli and will not, for example, snap at your hand moving within its reach; but if you but delicately touch the tip of one of its vibrissae, the reaction is so sudden that you will almost certainly be caught in the animal's well-equipped jaws. The vibrissae are arranged in two groups on each side of the face, one group on the cheek and the other near the snout. Nierembergius described them correctly over three centuries ago but ascribed to them no function other than adornment. Actually the whiskers are highly developed in all night prowlers and enable the animals to avoid collision with solid objects in their path. Each seta or bristle is a remarkable organ, provided at its base with an elaborate set of touch-sensitive nerve endings, so that the slightest contact even at the very tip of a bristle sets off the appropriate defense reaction. No wonder that I have been bitten more

39

than once through the burlap sack in which I was carrying an opossum.

The sense of smell, a most important faculty in foraging for food, is very well developed in the opossum. Much of its meager brain is given over to nerves controlling this function. The opossum has been said to be endowed with a sense of smell keen enough to identify human beings, but I have found no evidence of this. Hediger, who studied opossums in captivity, concluded that their sense of smell is not measurably so good as hunters generally think that it is.

The ears are, indeed, "thin and black, like a bat's," as Pinzón and other early authors would have it. In the Virginia opossum the ears are often tipped with a band of white of variable width; in the *Didelphis azarae* of the La Plata country the white band is very prominent.

The external ears serve not only to catch sounds but also to close the auditory canal against the ingress of insects when the opossum is asleep.

Most animals, not least the opossum, are inordinately sensitive to sounds. A light hand-clap or rustle of paper will often cause a marked reaction in captive animals, whereas a flash of light apparently goes unnoticed, just as with us lightning is less startling than thunder. The click of your camera shutter will be noticed by the opossum. Doubtless this sensitivity serves it well.

> 'Possum am a cunnin' thing
> He rambles in the dark
> Nothin' 'tall disturb his min'
> 'Cept to hyah ma bulldog bark.

The opossum's legs are short; the body round, stout, and fat. Its walk has been variously described as a waddle (Bachman) or a slow, meandering shuffle (Devoe). Coues was certainly mistaken when he described the opossum's gait as "single-footing," that is, progressing by lifting both feet of one side off the ground at the same time, alternating the sides. This conclusion is wrong even

though Audubon himself agreed with it. I am inclined to accept the conclusion of A. Brazier Howell, who has given special attention over many years to locomotion in animals. In a personal communication he writes:

I experimented with an opossum one afternoon on my lawn and could not get it out of a true trot, a peculiar, slinking action, both at lowest and at highest speed. Animals of broad beam and short legs, such as turtles, iguanas, opossums, badgers, are obliged to be well supported and cannot be shifting the center of gravity from side to side, in the pace or amble, as can a narrow one, or one with long legs. Hence opossums trot, even at the slowest tempo.

La Croix (1930) has sketched the opossum in a series of successive steps in walking.

As a climber the opossum is most adept, else how could he secure the persimmons made luscious by the first frosts of autumn? Note the five strong claws of the front toes; they are sharp like those of a squirrel.

The hind feet are different, as may be seen from Robert Hatt's photograph (p. 34), which explains what the earliest writers meant when they first saw the opossum's hind feet: "human hands similar to those of monkeys," whence the first name, *simivulpa*, "monkey-fox." The great toe stands out like a thumb, but it bears no nail; Shaw was in error when he had his artist put a claw on this member. The similarity to the human hand is heightened by the opposability of the great toe or "thumb"; that is, with its tip the animal can touch the tips of the other digits. Only man and the apes —and opossums—have opposable first digits.

Because of the laterally pointing great toe the opossum leaves unique footprints in mud or snow. That "thumb print" is unmistakable.

"Gray," you would say on first seeing a Virginia opossum. Correct. Gray is the general impression one carries away.

If one analyzes the hairs producing this over-all effect of gray, one notes that there are two kinds of hair: the fine, soft underfur and the coarse, long overhairs. The latter are pro-

Didelphis azarae, *the* comadreja *of the La Plata region, drawn by Carlos C. Wiedner. From Cabrera's and Yepes'* Historia natural Ediar: Mamíferos sud-americanos *(1940). By permission of Compañía Argentina de Editores.*

tective, reducing abrasion to the underfur that keeps the animal warm and also dry. Rain cannot wet the opossum's skin by virtue of the oiliness of the dense underfur. Such protection is common to many mammals, especially the aquatic beaver, seal, and otter, which are really never wet to the skin. If one adds a detergent to the water, the surface tension will be so reduced that the water will penetrate the fur. Place a duck in water that contains a detergent and the duck will sink.

The overhair of the opossum is white, tipped with black—the more black, the darker the animal. When the black amounts to more than two-thirds of the length of the hair, the specimen is spoken of as the "black phase." Whereas in northern latitudes opossums in the black phase are rare, numbering only one

in nine or ten, towards Florida this phase predominates. That is why Banks created a new subspecies for that region, his *Didelphis virginiana nigra.* In northern Mexico and southern Texas the black phase outnumbers the gray five to one, and the specimens tend to have longer tails with more black at the base. Taube (1942) states that the overhair of the local gray opossum in southwest Michigan, on microscopical examination, reveals a considerable amount of dark-brown pigment, verging on black. Museum specimens seem to change with time to a rather dominant brown color.

Blacks and grays may occur in the same litter. I have had a number such. Kenneth Cuyler reported a litter of five gray and three black belonging to a female caught in the

41

wild, and Brimley recorded a litter of seven black and seven gray. Krieg mentions capturing a litter of six of the Uruguayan *D. azarae* of which three were light, three dark.

Dark and light phases of the same species occur also among Australian marsupials, as illustrated, for example, in the brush-tailed *Trichosurus* shown in Plate IX of Troughton's book.

In all animals and plants, nature occasionally—perhaps once in a million individuals—leaves out or changes a hereditary factor. This results in the production of an individual differing in appearance from the typical. One common deviation from the normal is albinism, which has been described for most kinds of animals: white crabs, albino mice and rats, white crows, and even white whales. I have had opossums with pure white hair, but these were not pure albinos, for they had black ears and eyes; "albinotics" one might call them. Pure albinos have pink eyes, there

being no pigment to absorb the red color of the blood in the retina. Such pink-eyed albino opossums have been described.

Another mutation with which I am personally acquainted is the cinnamon color. Since one of these specimens also lacked the stiff overhairs, as seen in the figure on page 143, we have here a case of two genetic deviations from the normal in the same individual.

Is the odor of the opossum offensive to most people who come in contact with the animal? The answer cannot be stated categorically, for it depends on the species. I have personally found no one who objected to the odor of the Virginia opossum. John Burroughs stated that the "reputed fetidness of this animal is not objectionable to my senses."

Certain South American species of opossum are not so easily exonerated. Said De Léry: "The opossum is like the fox of Spain but smells much worse." *Puant*, the Cayenne

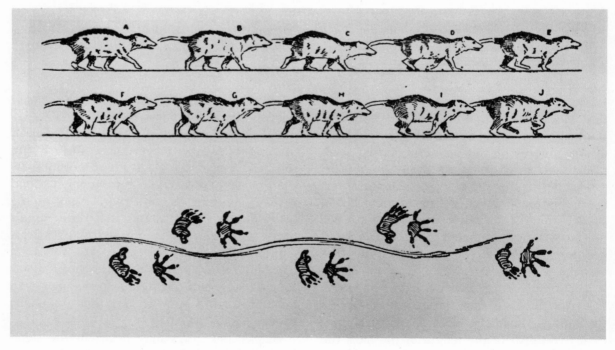

Above: opossum walking. Sketches by P. Magne de la Croix. Courtesy Journal of Mammalogy. *Below: footprints of opossum. From* Animal Tracks *(1943), by George F. Mason. By permission of William Morrow and Company, New York.*

42

French have hurled at him from the earliest times. *Didelphis azarae*, the *comedreya* of the Argentine, according to Cabrera and Yepes, is never captured for a pet, not only because of its stupidity but because of its vile odor, for which reason the species has been given another name also: *micuré*, signifying "fetid."

There is a popular notion that where there are opossums there will be no rats. "The plot thickens," C. E. McClung of the National Research Council wrote me during World War I; "the opossum has come into its own. To eradicate rats, keep 'possums—at least according to an authority from Indiana! . . . Will you tell me what you know about the alleged antipathy of the rat for the opossum? The matter has been referred to the National Research Council."

The same idea was prevalent also in Australia. In a letter to Ellis Troughton, author of *Furred Animals of Australia*, F. A. Pockley states that it is a popular belief that the long-nosed bandicoot keeps rats from one's premises. He continues: "I have trapped them and kept them in captivity for a time, to find out if there were anything in the statement that they would clear out rats. . . . I did not find that bandicoots kept them away, either bush rats or others."

I am personally of the opinion that the only rats that disappear because of opossums are the ones they kill and eat, for rat bones are a common constituent of opossum stomach contents.

In this chapter I have more or less taken the animal apart for closer analysis—which is one way of studying an animal or plant. I am not unmindful, however, of the oneness of a living organism and the advantages of studying a representative of a species of animal as a whole, especially as a living organism. The German naturalist Krieg has expressed this principle as follows:

Data on reproduction, life habits, and psyche are more important [for acquiring a correct mental picture of the animal] than details of the fur; habitat belongs to a description no less than skeleton, habits no less than teeth. The calling up of a name ought to arouse a complex of images of behavior and reactions like a character in a novel. The sportsman is often better at this than the scientist.

6

The Opossum at Home

SINCE water, food, and shelter are the opossum's major needs, he lives with preference along wooded water courses. This has long been known, in a general way, to hunters, trappers, and experienced outdoor naturalists such as Ernest Thompson Seton and Audubon. In recent decades several ecologists (students of plant and animal habitats) have gathered more exact data on the life habits of the opossum in the wild, demonstrating once again that science consists of proving the obvious. In the course of these studies, extensive censuses were made of populations of opossums in limited areas, of their individual movements from place to place, and of their feeding and nesting habits.

Most people have the idea that wild animals, free to roam afield, move far and wide over the landscape. From intensive banding studies, however, it has been found that this is not true. In these experiments animals are captured, either in live traps or with the aid of dogs, are marked, and are recaught some time later. In his Texas study, Daniel Lay, for example, discovered that of 116 opossums trapped in the selected area only one was taken as far as 750 feet from the stream, thirteen 400 to 600 feet, twenty-three 100 to 400 feet, and seventy-nine less than 100 feet.

The principle of the "home range" in animal life is now established for mammals, as is "territory" in bird life. Ornithologists have discovered that the male bird precedes the female to the breeding grounds and stakes out his claim, which he defends against all rivals. His assertive song is more of a challenge to combat than just the sweet love call traditionally extolled in lyric poems. A pair of birds will occupy the selected territory for an entire breeding season, often returning the following spring.

Mammals, too, remain for months and even for years within a restricted locality. Only one-half of Lay's recaptured specimens were itinerants from surrounding areas. The smaller the area, the more "strangers" are encountered; in Reynolds' two-square-mile reservation in Missouri only five opossums were squatters, the rest itinerants. One June I released into the cedar brakes about Austin, Texas, a dozen or more opossums no longer needed for observation. The next November some of these were discovered among opossums purchased from local boys.

The degree to which opossums show their preference for wooded plots over open country is illustrated by Lay's census: 1 opossum to 4 acres of woodland, against 1 to 146 acres of adjoining prairie.

In his travels in Peru, Tschudi seldom saw

44

opossums of the species *Didelphis impovida* in open fields, but members of his party were literally overrun by them at night when encamped in the woods. Alston said that he never saw an opossum in the open land in Costa Rica, though many are killed by automobiles on highways running through the forests.

The proportion of time which an animal spends on the ground and in trees varies with the species. The mouse opossum, *Didelphis murina,* is seldom seen on the ground; *Didelphis marsupialis* seldom in trees, except for its young, which prefer to climb.

Some animals exhibit a high degree of adaptability to changing habitats. An outstanding example is that of *Didelphis azarae* of the Argentine. The early settlers of that country, like the pioneers in the United States, changed the face of the landscape by stripping the forests of timber to build their houses and to clear the soil for cultivation. In the resulting man-made prairie of the Argentine, W. H. Hudson tells us, the only animals to survive were a small wild guinea pig, a few birds, and the Azara opossum, a species fitted for arboreal and not for prairie life. Years later, after a section of the city of La Plata had been planted with trees, among which were many densely foliated umbrella China trees *(Melia azedarach),* the displaced opossums resumed their arboreal habitat according to the ancestral fashion. The instinct to climb had not been eradicated by generations of disuse; to live in trees was still in the blood, or rather in the nervous system. This behavior is in accordance with everything we know about the laws of heredity.

An exact behavioral parallel to that of the Azara opossum is afforded by the sooty tern of Tern Island, in the Dry Tortugas, off the west coast of Florida. This bird normally nested in the low shrubs of the island, while its cousin, the noddy tern, in equal numbers, nested on the bare coral sands. Came a hurricane which swept away the shrubs; the fol-

A study in opossum habitat. Photograph by E. H. Sellards.

lowing breeding season the sooty tern made its nest on the ground beside those of the noddy. The present generations of sooties are back in the shrubs which have sprung up again. The terns did not become nomads, even when housing conditions were not exactly to the family's liking.

It is the general experience of hunters and trappers that more male opossums are taken than females, as the following table demonstrates. Items 1, 2, and 3 were reported by Davis (Brazil); 4 and 5 by Reynolds (Missouri); and 6 by Lay (East Texas).

SPECIES	MALES	FEMALES
1. *Didelphis marsupialis*	35	21
2. Philander opossum	43	32
3. Coluromys philander	5	5
4. *Didelphis virginiana*	620	456
5. *D. virginiana*	1245	940
6. *D. virginiana*	59	58

Assuming that in the opossum family the sexes are approximately equal in number, how shall we explain this differential? Does it mean that the females are more astute than the males in avoiding the hunter? Or shall we explain the preponderance of males in the catch on the basis of their greater mobility? The latter explanation is the more likely. Reynolds found that when the air temperature ranged around 41° F., the sex ratio among 686 individuals captured was 52 per cent males to 48 per cent females, an essentially "normal" sex ratio; but when the mean temperature dropped to 24° F., the ratio rose to 68 per cent males to 32 per cent females. Presumably in cold weather the males are the more likely to venture forth.

All nocturnal animals must find dens or build nests wherein to spend the day, safe from predaceous mammals and birds. Dens are of many varieties: crevices in the rocks, especially in limestone formations; cavities of hollow trees; spaces under piles of wood or lumber; abandoned squirrel nests; and warm retreats under people's houses, or even in their attics. Dens are lined with dry leaves and grass. In the Deep South the opossum may use Spanish moss, which hangs in graceful festoons from trees in the river bottoms. Some opossums and many Australian marsupials are expert nest-builders, and their nests are often hidden away in a network of interlacing vines.

One of the most skillful nest-builders is the Yawarri or mouse opossum of the Guiana forest, where the itinerant engineer-naturalist, R. W. G. Hingston, met and described it.

The Yawarri made a nest of moss, lined with dead leaves, about six inches long, four inches in diameter, with an opening in the side. This nest was fixed to a perpendicular root that dangled in mid-air over the forest creek about five feet above the water. The nest must have furnished absolute security, for it is most improbable that a snake or other reptile would descend a vertical root thirty or forty feet long, and no enemy except a man in a boat could reach it from below.

46

Perhaps the most remarkable and truly unique feature of nest-building among marsupials or any other order of mammals is the use of the tail in the transport of nesting materials. This phenomenon must be documented by citation of on-the-spot eyewitnesses in order to show that the unusual procedure is not the figment of some writer's imagination.

Opossum transporting a bundle of leaves in a downturned loop of the tail. Courtesy L. L. Pray and the Journal of Mammalogy.

In the 1846–48 edition of Waterhouse's *Natural History of Mammals* one finds a lithograph in color of a Bettongia or rat kangaroo with a bundle of grass held in the apical portion of its tail, used, "as Mr. Gould informs us, for carrying grasses, etc. with which these animals form their nest." Of the Tasmanian rat kangaroo, Gould said: "Their grassy nests were thick and cozy, built in a depression sheltered by a bush or large tuft of grass." A nest sent to the Tasmanian Museum was made entirely of fiberlike strips of stringy bark, every scrap of which had been carried over a quarter of a mile in the grip of the curled-up tail. A fine drawing of a brush-tailed rat kangaroo carrying nesting material in its prehensile tail may be found in Coupin's and Lea's *Romance of Animal Arts and Crafts* (1907).

Troughton refers to an episode occurring in the London Zoo, where one of the early Tasmanian rat kangaroo captives "was seen collecting a mass of straw and throwing it backward on to the tail which was stretched forward between the feet and then curled around the bundle which was thus carried for several hours while hopping about at night."

Troughton further quotes an account published by David Fleay in the *Victorian Naturalist* of 1932 concerning the sugar glider, the flying *Petaurus breviceps*. Individuals of this species were observed hanging upside down by the hind feet while biting off gum boughs. Transferring them by means of the forepaws, the glider twisted its tail around the bundle and ran with it into the nesting box. Troughton continues:

Similar habits were described to me some years ago by Miss Lily Ivey of Elizabeth Bay, Sydney, whose pet was a young one from an accidentally killed parent. Small twigs of gum tree were usually placed in the cage. . . . One day the animal astonished its mistress by bustling down with a bundle of leaves and twigs held close to the body by the tail which was twisted tightly around it. The bundle was quite five inches long by about three in width . . . and with considerable trouble he got the burden through the small entrance, then returned to collect small pieces dropped on the way.

As early as 1872, G. Lincecum records the following observation: "I have seen them [the Virginia opossums] carrying into their holes at the approach of cold weather bundles of dry leaves rolled up in their tail; they understand the rigors of the coming spells of cold weather, and they prepare for it by making themselves a good warm bed."

Hediger saw his tame opossum carry excelsior in a loop of the tail; L. L. Pray gave an exact account of a captive juvenile carrying leaves in the same manner. Hesselschwert and Reynolds made similar but more casual observations on opossums in the wild. Tate saw a "short-tailed South American opossum drag with its tail a piece of newspaper which, it was presumed, was intended for its nest." This incident recalls Troughton's amusing story of a pound note, then equivalent to a five-dollar bill, which disappeared from a timber camp. The resulting strained feelings among the lumbermen were resolved only when, on felling a nearby tree, the note was found in the nest of a brush-tailed marsupial rat. Pieces of paper or rag for nest-building were frequently taken from camps or houses.

In final proof of the strange use of the tail, the opossum's "behind hand" as Ernest Thompson Seton called it, I quote a realistic description by Luther Smith, published in the *Journal of Mammalogy* (1941):

In the early morning of August 4, 1938, I had an opportunity to watch at close range an opossum in the act of gathering and transporting leaves, presumably for an underground nest. I was hunting squirrels in the woods of Bollinger County, in southeastern Missouri, when my attention was attracted by the rustling in the dry leaves near by. The noise was made by a young opossum slightly more than half grown. The animal came out of a hole in the ground about eight feet from where I stood and proceeded to select small mouthfuls of two or three leaves each. The leaves were taken out of the mouth by the forepaws and passed back along the abdomen to a position in front of the thighs. There they remained momentarily while the front feet were placed on the ground and the hind feet were brought up to take them and slide them along the tail into a loop in that member, which is ordinarily thought of as a means of support by suspension but which in this case was sustaining the hind quarters above ground while the hind feet were being used to place the leaves in the loop.

About six or eight mouthfuls were handled in this way. The action was rapid, and the leaves were in almost continuous motion from the time they were picked up from the ground until they came to rest in the coil of the tail. After the loop was filled, the opossum chose a last mouthful and, with its tail extended almost horizontally except for the loop which held the bundle of leaves, proceeded into the hole in the ground.

Soon the animal returned, and when it first came up the tail was nearly straight with the end dragging on the ground. When first leaves were picked up, the loop was formed in the tail, and the process of gathering a bundle of leaves was repeated. The opossum made four trips in about ten minutes. It paid no attention to me, although it faced me in returning to the hole. At no time was the animal over fifteen feet away. I wished heartily for a motion picture camera.

During its fifth trip for leaves, I walked over and put my foot in the hole from which it had emerged. The animal dropped the unfinished roll of leaves, bristled, and advanced to attack, snarling and showing its teeth. It snapped at my shoe, which I extended, and after more snarling turned and ran clumsily though quite rapidly away, presumably to another burrow.

It may be accepted as fact, then, that the opossum and other marsupial animals use their tail as described. In contrast to this well-demonstrated phenomenon, I call attention to the legend of the animated sled, current in European and Asiatic folklore for over two thousand years. It was Du Pratz who brought the legend to Louisiana and attached it to the opossum: "When the female is about to give birth to the young, she, in company with the male, goes in search of fine grass. After accumulating what is necessary, the female lies on her back, the male puts the grass between her paws and drags her by the tail to the nest."

In Europe, ever since the days of Pliny, this pretty story concerned the marmot or ground hog and sometimes also the badger. The German-Swiss poet and novelist Gottfried Keller over a century ago wrote a playful poem on this theme for the delectation of his juvenile audience.

So far as I have been able to find out, Du Pratz is the only writer on early American natural history who has mentioned this animated-sledge mode of bringing in bedding material. Other authors doubtless considered the tale simply an amusing figment of the popular imagination. The story recalls the legend of the egg-carrying rats, told and illustrated in La Fontaine's fable "The Two Rats, the Fox and the Egg." To keep the egg from falling into the keen and eager snout of

An opossum joins battle with a deadly moccasin. Photograph by Underwood & Underwood.

48

The victor, Br'er Possum. He will shortly eat the body of his foe. Photograph by Underwood & Underwood.

Sir Reynard, the rats had to transport it to a safe retreat. How this was done was illustrated for La Fontaine by the famous artist Doré. It is interesting to note that for better purchase the rat acting as egg wagon has its tail wound, opossum fashion, around the base of its partner's tail.

Doré's humorous drawing is, of course, highly fanciful; but the basic phenomenon E. W. Gudger, historian of curious facts and legends in natural history, has not been willing to dismiss as wholly imaginary. In his essay "How Rats Transport Eggs" he quotes eyewitnesses who claimed to have seen some

such behavior of rats transporting eggs, and he traces the story back to a Persian manuscript of the thirteenth century. Presumably it goes back much further.

Gudger also cites a case of two rats that lay in wait until a certain hen left the nest cackling, when they would appear and cart off the egg. A parallel is offered by a recent "Letter to the Editor" (in 1950) about two opossums that sat next to a hen waiting for her to lay. Strange companions to a hen! And just how two opossums would go about dividing a raw egg, I leave to the reader's imagination.

Three-month-old opossums hanging by their tails. Courtesy C. P. Fox and Life.

7

And Thereby Hangs a Possum

IT WAS THE POSSESSION of a brood pouch which gave the newly discovered animal its news value for several centuries. In the course of time, however, the opossum's prehensile tail came in for its share of attention. Here again observed facts were improved upon and ridiculously exaggerated. In this chapter I shall first describe the well-observed uses which the animal finds for its tail in its various activities and then trace some additional fantastic uses that yarn-telling travelers have accredited to it. As none of the fictitious uses is more unusual or unexpected than the authenticated use of the tail for gathering nesting material, as described in the preceding chapter, the need for precise observation and experimentation in sifting truth from error is again evident.

The scaly, naked, ratlike character of the tail is reflected in the names attached to the species—*Beutelratte, Boschrot, rat de bois*—words which seem superficially correct but are zoologically wrong, for the American opossum and the Australian marsupial rat are not rodents.

There can be no doubt that the prehensile function of the tail is of real use to its bearer whether this be opossum, rodent, or spider monkey. With tail well wrapped about a branch, cane, or one's finger, the fattest opos-

sum can support its weight, although for a short period of time only. No one has ever seen a Virginia opossum "rest" in such a position. An exceptional case of extended suspension of the pygmy possum was observed by the Australian ornithologist Mattingley, who related it to Troughton. The opossum was found in a dormant state of complete hibernation. Trying to arouse it, Mattingley hung the animal on a twig by its prehensile tail; it grasped the belly fur with its paws and remained automatically suspended for several hours, when it awoke.

Correlated with this function of the tail are two structures: the strong development of muscles on the under side of the tail, and the stout blood vessels supplying these muscles. The living opossum carries its tail more or less curled downwards in the ventral direction, never upwards, as Shaw has wrongly pictured it in his textbook. The slow curling up of the tail I have always regarded as a sign of approaching death.

Even in the pouch young, long before any use for the function has arisen in the life of the animal, the tail will, on stimulation, curl downward. Juvenile opossums seem better at hanging by the tail than older individuals. In a young opossum which he raised and closely observed, Hediger noted a decline in this ability with the maturity of the animal.

The statement of Wood, who claimed that the opossum could hang with only 5 per cent of its tail wound around a twig or rod, is certainly an exaggeration. This fallacy has far too often become congealed in drawings and in taxidermy groups, as for example the steel engraving in Godman's *American Natural History* (1846).

How the tail helps the opossum in climbing has been well stated by R. K. Enders, who has observed numerous species in the field:

There appears to be little understanding of the use of the tail, for opossums are mounted and drawn as hanging by this member, the extreme tip of which is wrapped tightly around a small twig. This the writer has never observed in nature. A captive specimen showed remarkable strength when the tip encountered a strand of wire, but usually the grip of the tail around small twigs and vines is not very strong. However, the tail is invaluable to this opossum (*Didelphis marsupialis etensis*) as it is to *Marmosa* and many other prehensile-tailed mammals as a safety device. While treading its aerial highways, the tail is curled loosely around a limb or vine along which the animal is passing, and it may be clamped around a support with telling effect if the limb is shaken. Should the animal lose its footing the tail does much to prevent a fall. The "hands" of *Didelphis* make it very sure-footed on slender vines, but less so on larger vines and branches and it is here that the tail is most effectively used. The writer has never seen this marsupial use the tail as a brace in sitting (after the manner of the kangaroo tribe), or seen it assume the "tripod" attitude.

What is true for the opossum holds also for rats and mice: they, too, use their tails as safety devices in getting about.

The climbing propensities of the opossum make this animal a nuisance in warm climates where the houses are lightly built and rooms (including the kitchen) are readily accessible. I have this observation in a letter from J. F. Tristán concerning some Costa Rican opossums: "Being a night prowler, its furtive movements have been associated in the minds of the ignorant with ghosts and witchcraft. It invades houses, climbing nimbly over the furniture, examining every corner for food. In these activities it often upsets dishes much to the annoyance of the occupants."

Alston goes into some detail in these matters:

The first of all mammals of Costa Rica with which the newly arrived foreigner has an opportunity of making a near if not agreeable acquaintance is the Long-eared Opossum. In the towns there are few houses that are not infested by these hideous beasts. Often strangers are aroused from their slumbers by an unwonted sound, which is really caused by these brutes running with heavy tread over the thin boarding of the roof, or by upsetting dishes, plates, and other household utensils during a visit to the larder or kitchen; and the said stranger often fancies that a burglary is being attempted, springs from his bed and grasps his weapons. But if he makes inquiry next day as to the cause of the alarm, he receives one answer, "Senor, es el Zorro." Zorro means properly a fox in Spanish; but the colonists gave the name to the Opossum because it works the same mischief among the poultry in Costa Rica as the fox does in Europe, though it cannot compare with the latter in respect to quickness and cunning.

For the scientist studying the opossum, the tail serves as a convenient "handle." If it is necessary to catch hold of the animal more firmly, one sets it on the floor, restraining it by the tail; then with a quick movement of the free hand one grasps the animal by the nape of the neck, firmly and with determination, for here hesitation is likely to be unwholesome. In carrying the opossum by the tail, one must not forget that it can climb up its tail till its jaws come in contact with the captor's hand, for the opossum is extremely supple, doubling up with the greatest ease. In fact, it sleeps in that position.

Folklore places no limit on exaggerated uses for the opossum's tail. Here is a quotation from the book by Dumont de Montigny,

Allen's opossum (Metachirops fuscogriseus). Note tail wrapped about branch for greater security.
Courtesy Robert K. Enders, Swarthmore College.

an officer of the Compagnie des Indes in New Orleans:

The instinct with which it hunts is very curious. After having caught a small bird and killed it, it is very careful not to eat it; it neatly places it in a fine uncovered place near some large tree; then climbs into that tree &, hanging by its tail to the branch which is nearest the bird, it patiently waits thus until some flesh-eating bird should come to carry it off. Then it pounces upon it and makes prey of both the one and the other.

This must have sounded most thrilling to the gay Parisians of the day.

The story reminds one of the clever cormorant, which is reputed to scatter bits of fish into the water in order to attract more fish to the surface—a story based on three readily ascertainable facts: (1) cormorants eat fish; (2) their table manners are bad, for they drop crumbs on the dining-room floor; (3) fish come to gather the crumbs.

53

Ergo: Cormorants are smart, like people. So with De Montigny's opossum: (1) it has a tail; (2) it hangs by the tail when occasion warrants; (3) it eats birds. *Ergo:* The stupidest of mammals is represented as planting bait to secure its dinner.

Pennant cribbed the yarn for his great textbook of zoology, with the additional gratuitous statement that "it continues frequently hanging with its head down." John D. Godman, physician and naturalist (a combination very common in his day), tells the De Montigny tale in his *American Natural History* and then adds that the tail enables the opossum to suspend itself while rifling eggs from birds' nests and while gathering fruit. Richard Harlan, M.D., in his *Fauna Americana* (1825) also elaborates on the story, but Dr. James De Kay, to whom Harlan dedicated his volume, cautiously omitted the reference from his *Natural History of New York* (1842). Other popular natural histories, for example Fitzinger's, keep the story alive. Even so scientific an observer as Dr. Barton, in a letter to Reimerus of Hamburg, repeated the statement without question. He wrote: "He is a good climber and his strong prehensile tail enables him, by supporting himself from the branch of a tree, to take the eggs (and perhaps the young birds) from the nest upon a branch immediately below."

The most fertile imagination in rounding out this tale was that of W. Saville-Kent, who wrote the article on marsupials for the *Standard Library of Natural History* (1908): "While assimilating his meal of flesh or fruit, Brer 'Possum likes to have all four hands at liberty, his hind feet being also graspers; and so he twists his tail round a convenient branch and hanging perdu, leisurely enjoys his feast." This version is also to be found in the *Encyclopedia Americana* of 1936. Perhaps Author Saville-Kent got his idea from the drawing in J. G. Wood's *Animate Creation* of a crab-eating opossum hanging by the

tail from a limb and holding a bird in its mouth.

This bit of nature lore is not of recent origin, for Du Tertre mentioned it in 1654; to quote:

> [The animal is also] called *caregüiya*, *maritacaca* & *ospason* according to the language of the country where it is met with. . . . It has two moustaches, like a cat. It has a tail twice as long as its body, half furry, half bare, like that of a rat; the natives assure me that it is so strong that it may hang by its tail to the branches of the trees. It throws itself from tree to tree with marvellous agility.

If this detail had originated in Central or South America instead of the Antilles, where Du Tertre lived, I should have decided that perhaps the traveler Du Tertre had confused the opossum with the spider monkey, the champion acrobat of the forest, for spider monkeys have the most mobile and efficient of all prehensile tails, as frequenters of our zoos well know.

The zoologist Shaw did not miss this report; he wrote: "The opossum is an expert climber of trees and readily passes by means of its clinging tail, from bough to bough in the manner of a monkey." Young readers of the *Penny Magazine* were instructed in the same pseudo science, and Bewick, the famous woodcut artist, in his *General History of Quadrupeds* conveniently combines the De Montigny and the Du Tertre points of "unnatural history":

> The opossum is a slow, helpless animal, when on the ground; but climbs trees with great ease and quickness; sometimes conceals itself among the branches and surprises the birds that come within reach. It frequently hangs suspended by the tail, and in that situation, watches for its prey, which it darts upon with great agility. . . . By means of its tail, the opossum flings itself from one tree to another.

The American originator of some of the reports just recited, was outdone by the

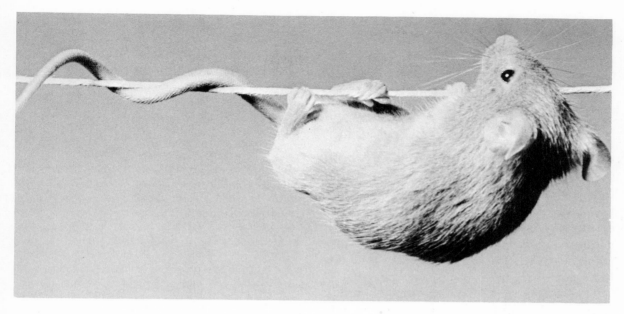

Mice, like opossums, sometimes use their tails for added support. This mouse's tail comes in handy as he clings precariously to a tight wire. Courtesy Irving Galinsky and Life.

natives of the East Indies. One reads in Edward Griffith's English edition of Cuvier's *Animal Kingdom:* "In the Moluccas where they [the phalangers] seek insects and fruits in trees, when they see a man they suspend themselves by the tail and it is possible to make them fall through lassitude by continuing to stare at them for some time."

This old yarn, I am reminded by the Texas writer J. Frank Dobie, has its American counterpart in Davie Crockett's method of "grinning a coon out of a tree." I have run down the source of Cuvier's "information." The responsible reporter was the Rev. François Valentyn, who was, according to the title page of his voluminous work (1726), "late preacher of God's word in Amboina, Banda, etc." In Book Five of his third volume, which treats of *Animals in Amboina,* he gives many details concerning the marsupial which the Malays call *coescoes,* "a most unique animal from the family of weasels but the size of a grown cat." From the natives Pastor Valentyn received the following account:

Nothing is more remarkable than the natives' method of catching them. This is brought about when the animal is sitting in a tree, by looking at it intently and so long that, though the tail may be wound about the branch or limb of the tree, it falls to the ground because of fright. It also, as soon as it sees a man, holds onto a limb by its tail, hangs and rocks back and forth, without appearing to notice the intruder. Those who are accustomed to catch the beast remain stock-still, gazing at it more intently, whereat it forgets to hold on with its tail, tumbles from its height, and remains lying in a faint for some time, when it is killed or taken alive. The Amboinese believe that the faculty of looking a *coescoes* out of a tree is a unique one, and certainly not all who try can carry it out; and there are experts at the business.

Numerous writers have called attention to the disagreeable appearance of the opossum's tail; Pennant (1793) thought it looked like the body of a snake. This idea has recently been enlarged upon by the animal behaviorist Hediger, author of *Wild Animals in Captivity,* who remarked that, since an angry opossum, facing an enemy, coils and uncoils its tail, the resemblance of this organ to a

55

snake might have some defensive value by frightening the enemy. This interpretation seems to make sense, since it is moving objects that animals see best.

There is a legend that converts the opossum tail into a veritable fishing rod. In *The Animal Kingdom*, Robert Kerr's story of the crab-eating opossum, *Didelphis cancerivora*, which is said to fish with its tail, reads as follows: "When it cannot reach the crabs in their holes with its paws, it introduces its prehensile tail to hook them out; and in this attempt it often gets pinched, on which occasion it emits a cry, somewhat like that of mankind, which is heard a great distance; but its ordinary voice is a kind of grunt."

There is current in many parts of South America a legend that the jaguar uses its tail as a lure in fishing. The first to mention this was the German scientist J. R. Rengger, who lived in Paraguay for eight years and wrote a book on the mammals of that country. This legend E. W. Gudger has traced, citing eyewitnesses; and he found that the story may be more than a legend, that it may have a high degree of authenticity. The reader is referred to Gudger's extensive article "Does the Jaguar Use His Tail as a Lure in Fishing." He cites no European authorities, but the passage quoted from Kerr would seem to indicate that the alleged technique of animals was known to European folklore. I note also that Barton's German correspondent, Reimerus, raised the question, quoting Buffon; hence I conclude that the legend is very old and probably European in origin.

The climax of the present theme is furnished by Topsell, translating Gesner in *The Historie of Foure-Footed Beastes* (1607). The quotation concerns co-operation among mice:

And as their wisdome is admirable in this provision, so also is their love to be commended one to another, for falling into a vessell of Water or other deepe thing, out of which they cannot ascend againe of themselves, they help one another, by letting downe their tailes, and if their tailes be to short, then they lengthen them by this meanes, they take one anothers taile in their mouth, and so hang two or 3 in lingth untill the Mouse which was fallen downe take hold of the neathermost, which being performed, they al of them draw her out.

The legends cited in this chapter illustrate the persistence of bizarre notions of natural history which, arising in the minds of ignorant and superstitious natives, were passed on to credulous Europeans. Nevertheless we must not criticize the pioneers in the study of nature, amateurs as they were anyway, for they had neither the facilities nor the scientific background for checking their statements. Besides, the real authorities, leading scientists of their time (Linnaeus and Buffon; Pennant, Shaw, and Kerr; Barton and Cuvier) accepted and repeated many of the statements which writers frankly admitted stemmed from the untutored natives.

8

Chicken Thief

MANY of the birds and beasts of the field have undeserved reputations for economic harm. Their human detractors usually see but one side of the wild beasts' lives, focusing attention solely on the damage done —which may be quite real—at the same time failing to give the animal credit for compensatory benefits. The coyote, for example, makes costly inroads on the ranchman's flock of sheep; so Congress and the United States Fish and Wildlife Service are petitioned to eradicate the pest. When this has been thoroughly accomplished, prairie dogs and ground squirrels, normal prey for the coyote, multiply unduly and destroy the sheep's pasturage, leaving the ranchman poorer than before. The farmer makes war on hawks because an occasional feathered predator swoops down with evil intent upon his chicken yard. What the farmer overlooks is the fact that hawks, along with owls, are indispensable in keeping populations of rats and mice in check. All of which reminds me of Abraham Lincoln's epigram: "It has ever been my experience that folks who have no vices have few virtues."

The opossum, indicted as a willful invader of henroosts, has been unanimously accused by all the early amateur naturalists except, of course, those who preceded the importation of *Galla domestica* into the New World. The domestic hen is strictly a Eurasian species, stemming originally from the wild jungle fowl of India. The first chickens, I believe, were brought to America by Columbus on his second voyage. His physician, Dr. Chanca, reported that at the Canary Islands the ships took on water, animals (including fowls and pigeons), and seeds. All subsequent colonists seem to have brought fowl with them as a matter of course. These multiplied rapidly. Three decades after the discovery of America, Oviedo, vivid writer and extensive traveler in Spanish America, wrote a damaging indictment of the *churcha* as a chicken thief. Before the end of the century the opossum's fondness for chickens had become proverbial.

De Léry, Dutch Protestant missionary to Brazil, characterized the opossum in these words: "The *carigue* . . . generally brings forth half a dozen or more young at a litter, which is too many by five for such ravenous vermin as they are; for they destroy all manner of poultry and climb up the trees and houses, too, in the nighttime for prey; in short, there's hardly a bird that can 'scape 'em."

Linnaeus naïvely asserted in his *Systema naturae* that "the opossum lives on chickens and sweet herbs, climbs trees; pursued by dogs it feigns death." Three and one-half centuries after Oviedo, H. W. Bates in *The Naturalist on the River Amazons* harped on the same theme: "It is very difficult to rear poultry in this country on account of these small opossums, scarcely a night passing, in some parts, in which fowls are not attacked by them." The late Morris Steggerda, student of the modern Mayan Indians, relates seeing children and even adults of that tribe soak the opossum with kerosene and ignite it "in punishment for stealing chickens."

Now and again one reads that opossums kill chickens wantonly, far beyond their needs, merely to suck the blood. Oviedo was perhaps the first to publish this accusation:

While slaughtering the hens, the young opossums come out of the pouch also to suck blood. Fifteen to twenty hens are killed and their blood sucked. If a person comes out with a light, the mother hides the young in the double pouch and flees; but block her exit and she climbs to hide. In this way one has caught them and found young ones in the pouch attached to the teats.

For the present we shall pass over the error that the young, supposedly attached to the teats, are let out to suck the victims' blood. But such is the natural history of the period —partly right.

This alleged practice of opossums' killing numbers of chickens in a single raid crops up in the literature again and again. I have a notion that such depredations should be charged to weasels rather than to opossums, the latter, because of their sluggishness, being the more likely of the two to get caught. Such raids of wanton destruction do actually seem to be a common practice of the predaceous and carnivorous marsupial of Tasmania locally known as the "tiger cat," if we are to believe Louisa Anne Meredith, who wrote about such "wholesale murder among poultry": "On many a dark night did papa and I jump up, scuffle on some clothes and rush out

at the sound of piteous squawking from the henhouse or duckpen. An unfortunate bird is gripped by the throat, and some of its blood sucked; then another and another, till a dozen or more fine young turkeys or fowls strew the floor." Mrs. Meredith adds that many cats "creep in before the fowls are at roost and abide their time."

The evidence against the opossum is complete and convincing. He is guilty. He is a chicken thief. Thousands of eyewitnesses could be summoned against him right here in the United States. The only question is: How guilty? I am inclined to attest that, in proportion to his deserts, he is about as guilty as Jean Valjean, sent to the galleys for stealing a loaf of bread. Many services to man can be chalked up on the credit side of the opossum's ledger. An unbiased judge is Professor Enders, who spent many months as a roving naturalist in Central America, where he became acquainted with numerous species of opossum. In the following quotation he points out' that there are plenty of extenuating circumstances which lessen the opossum's guilt and place some of the blame on the carelessness of man.

Canal employes and natives alike [in Panama] rise up at the mention of the opossum to assure one of its deadly raids upon domestic poultry as on the game birds. The writer observed such a raid at Alhajuela. A medium sized opossum took a month-old chick away from a hen at 5:30 a.m. The native to whom the chicken belonged said that the opossums were a source of constant loss. Nevertheless, he permitted the hens with the chicks to spend the night under the floor of the shed in a situation which invited attack by all flesheaters, including rats of which there were many. The usual method of "housing" chickens is to erect a few poles on uprights about six feet above ground and trust that no opossums, owls, Tayra, or cats are hungry enough to eat them.

It is the writer's belief that these attacks are greatly exaggerated. If members of this group are really such blood-thirsty, poultry- and bird-killers, why did the crippled "pavo" remain undisturbed on her nightly roost when many

Chicken thief.

Didelphis were seen about? She roosted un-molested from March 10 to July 3. True, there was much fruit available at this time, but the very type of poultry roost used rather discredits any great propensity for killing on the part of the rather stupid opossum.

In a lighter vein I offer a humorous gem for which I am indebted to that literary sleuth J. Frank Dobie, who tells me that the manuscript "Reminiscences of James Buck-ner Barry," from which the following quota-tion has been taken, is on deposit in the Li-brary of the University of Texas:

I will here give an incident as told by a negro man. While many doubted the story none who were familliar with the customs and habits of the opossum would or could take the responsibility to comdemn what the negro told. He was come-ing home early one morning from his wifes house before day, when near the barn yard he met an old opossum in the road with one chicken in her mouth another in the coil of her tail dragging it, some [of] her young ones on her back others following by her side. The only evidence the negro had to back his story, was he brought in the old opossom, her young ones, and two chickens. But the smart ellicks always stand ready to find fault of any proposition with-out honest considderation, or endorse any propo-sition without consideration, if that propposition be popular, and accused the negro [of] fitting up the chicken part of the story to make it appear it was the oposom getting away with the chickings and not him.

Far be it from me to take sides in this con-troversy!

While chicken meat may be the *pièce de résistance* of the opossum's menu, it is by no means its sole food. What is the real ex-tent of the opossum's chicken thievery? What is the verdict of the ecologists who have

A hen cackles in terror as an opossum closes in for the kill. Photograph by Underwood & Underwood.

studied carefully the food habits of the opossum? In other words, what proportion of the opossum's sustenance is derived from birds and their eggs?

Harold C. Reynolds has collected data which partially answer these questions. Observations were made of the food habits of opossums caught in a partly wooded area two square miles in extent adjoining the city of Columbia, Missouri. Most of the opossums trapped in this area were nonresidents, that is, were merely passing through, hence may be presumed to have had access to residential premises and their garbage cans. Even so, remains of birds or their eggs were found in only 8.9 per cent of 259 "scats" (droppings) and of 68 stomachs of opossums killed for the market. Empty eggshells and meatless chicken bones which opossums pick up would account for some of the contents. Dead birds,

too, are relished by the opossum and are much more easily secured than live ones by so slow and awkward a beast. The opossum hardly has the agility for much bird-catching. Nevertheless, Ned Dearborn's studies based on the stomach content of 23 opossums showed that the remains of birds constituted 24.7 per cent, a percentage larger than that found by other investigators, as for example Taube, who recovered remains of miscellaneous birds in only about one-third of 130 opossums captured in Michigan but found the total quantity of bird remains to be less than 10 per cent. Remains of pheasants were found only once. Taube also maintains that opossums have to learn to crack an egg and eat the contents—a conclusion reached by experiments with two captive specimens presented with pheasants' eggs.

On the credit side of the ledger, Dearborn

60

reports that insects made up 16.7 per cent of the volume of stomach contents examined, and mammals, mostly rats and mice, 23.2 per cent. In East Texas, D. W. Lay found that insects made up 45 per cent of the opossum's diet. Reynolds reported that 87.6 per cent of his cases had in their stomachs the remains of insects, representing scores of species.

In the balance of nature, therefore, the opossum plays a role beneficial to man and is much more of an asset than a liability.

The arboreal mouse opossum (Marmosa) depends exclusively on insects and fruit. It not infrequently happens that one of these diminutive animals, hidden in a bunch of bananas, gets loaded on a banana boat and carried as stowaway to the United States. Miss Marjorie Shanafelt, of the State Museum of Nebraska, has written charmingly about one of these murine mothers and her brood of six young ones.

Since the holds of banana boats are usually held at 57°F., the most favorable temperature for the ripening process, there has been much speculation as to how the delicate tropical organisms survive the long journey. Enders has given the most plausible explanation. Since ripening bananas consume much oxygen, the hold must be ventilated; hence fresh air must be drawn in continuously. It seems quite probable that our marmosa migrates to the air intake and lives on insects brought in by the stream of warmer air from the outside. Numerous reports on "banana stowaways" appeared in *Science* in 1930.

Unlike the marmosa, the Virginia opossum does not live entirely on animal food, but rather on a mixed diet including fruits and

Opossum in search of grubs, a useful occupation. Courtesy W. J. Hamilton, Jr.

seeds. Broken down into order of frequency and relative volume, these foods make up a table like this.

FREQUENCY	VOLUME
Insects	Insects
Fruits	Mammals
Invertebrates (other than insects)	Reptiles
	Seeds
Mammals	Fruits
Reptiles	Birds and eggs
Grains	Invertebrates
Birds and eggs	(other than insects)

This is a little more substantial than the "sweet herbs" of which Linnaeus spoke. The list includes grains, some of which may be procured raccoon or crow fashion, by pulling up the farmer's seedling corn.

There is a tradition that the opossum is inordinately fond of persimmons:

> 'Possum up a 'simmon tree
> 'Possum don't know nuffin'.

Audubon painted his opossums, male and female, on a branch of the persimmon tree, a device imitated by others. Someone has pointed out that the geographical distribution of the Virginia opossum and that of the persimmon tree very nearly coincide.

In the same region grows the unpretentious pokeberry. So far as the stomach content of the opossum is concerned, the pokeberry (Phytolacca) is said to make up twice the volume of the persimmon diet; but there may be a catch in this, inasmuch as the opossum, unlike the raccoon, rarely swallows the persimmon pit, which tends to lower the score for this fruit in comparison with the rival pokeberry.

These remarks on food habits relate chiefly to the Virginia opossum but hold for most of the members of the genus Didelphis. Many species know how to find, in addition to the items mentioned, such prey as crayfish or, at the seashore, crabs. The web-footed water opossum or yapok (Chironectes) makes a specialty of shrimp and crayfish, though in captivity it will accept meat as a substitute. And the substitute need not be chicken.

To many persons the opossum is known only as a chicken thief. I trust that the facts presented in this chapter will put Br'er Possum in a better light.

9

Playing Possum

IF YOU HUNT YOUR OPOSSUM in the daytime, you will search favorite retreats such as hollow logs or tree trunks in the woodsy bottoms. In rocky terrain you will poke into cracks and crannies in the ground. You probably would not reach into the possible hide-out with bare hands, as did a hunting companion of mine in the limestone hills of central Texas. This hero of many expeditions would at times run his hand slowly along the side of the burrow until he felt the soft fur. Then with a sudden vicelike grip he would pinion the quarry and pull it into the light. Ordinarily you will have provided yourself with a tough forked stick with which you will twist a hold in the opossum's dense fur. Despite strong resistance you are usually able to draw forth the unwilling creature.

While still in the retreat there is no "playing possum." Instead, your efforts are met with angry growls from the dark depths of the recess. Your opossum faces the entrance, powerful jaws armed with long canines reinforcing the show of courage. But once you have pulled him out of his den, he gives up and, so long as you are near, he lies still as death.

When you hunt at night, your dogs may flush an opossum out foraging on his favorite trail and send him scurrying up the nearest tree. If then you shake him off the limb on which he has taken refuge, you will see the same behavior of playing dead, which often deceives even the dogs that have pounced upon him. Leave him and he will soon recover and waddle away.

Although "playing possum" is a proverbial term in the United States, the phenomenon is by no means limited to this American marsupial. The feigning of death is known throughout the animal kingdom, and certain aspects of it may be observed in man himself. The experimental study of the cataleptic state in animals, it is believed, will do much to explain similar states in man. For this reason we should attempt to place the death-feigning of the opossum in its proper setting as a natural phenomenon in mammals, birds, amphibia, and many kinds of animals without backbones.

The opossum's method of counterfeiting death is also practiced by some Australian marsupials and some members of the dog tribe, notably the fox. Interest in the phenomenon dates far back in European history, as attested, for example, by a twelfth-century drawing of a death-feigning fox surrounded by birds. This was reproduced by P. A. Robin in his *Animal Lore in English Literature*.

In his delightful *Naturalist in La Plata*,

W. H. Hudson describes death-feigning of the pampas fox, *Canis azarae,* as well as the Argentine opossum, *Didelphis azarae,* and is inclined to judge the fox the better actor of the two.

A fox caught in a trap fights savagely at first but by and by relaxes his efforts, drops to the ground and apparently yields up the ghost. The deception is so well carried out that dogs are consistently taken in by it, and no one not previously acquainted with the clever trickery, but would at once pronounce the creature dead, and worthy of some praise for having perished in so brave a spirit. When one withdraws a little way from the feigning fox and watches him, he will see the deceiver get up slowly and cautiously when his foes are at a safe distance. The fox, however, need not be touched but only taken unawares to cause him to fall into a swoon, as when a man on horseback comes upon him suddenly.

A Negro-English proverb has it: "What de fox found out de possum knowed long ago."

Naturalists have also observed identical behavior in the dingo or wild dog of Australia. This rapacious animal is the only sizable representative of death-feigners among the higher mammals, that is, those above the marsupials in the evolutionary scale. One description of the dingo's "going dead" is almost a paraphrase of Hudson's account of the fox:

The poor brute will keep up the pretense even when its head has been broken. Some cases are known where such an animal has been left for dead . . . but during the night it has managed to crawl away into its native haunts without having given one sign of life during the whole time it was being beaten to death. This would seem to need one kind of courage at least.

The description of the death-feigning of opossum, fox, and dingo applies also to birds. An owl held captive for fifteen hours fell into a swoon whenever anyone approached. Prentiss relates an experience with a turkey buzzard which he had winged with a shot and driven to the foot of a tree. On being approached, the bird disgorged the fetid contents of its crop—its first defense reaction—whereupon it fell over as though dead. The "dead" bird was brought home and laid down outdoors. Imagine the astonishment of the naturalist-huntsman later when he saw the buzzard wandering about the barnyard, where it readily repeated its previous performance at the slightest alarm.

Howard Vogel tells of coming upon an adult buzzard brooding two newly hatched young. The mother, when disturbed in the nest, feigned death and repeated this act on several occasions.

What shall we say, however, to the report of the Texas naturalist Lincecum, who claims that he saw a turkey buzzard fly down, make an opossum go dead, then pick out his eyes and tear away pieces of the victim's neck and shoulder? While this item and some others in Lincecum's writings make me dubious concerning his reliability as an observer, he may in this instance actually have seen what he reported.

Like mammals and birds, reptiles too simulate death. Thomas Barbour, noted Harvard University zoologist, naturalist, and traveler, furnished the following examples in his *Reptiles and Amphibians: Their Habits and Adaptations:*

Varanus exanthematicus, a lizard from the Congo, turns on its back and, seizing one of its paws in its mouth, lies perfectly still in this apparently uncomfortable position. Another classical example is the hog-nosed snake, which turns over on its back, opens wide its mouth, hangs out its tongue, and looks as if it had just died in agony. The only mistake it makes is that, if it is reversed, it promptly turns over on its back again. The giant *Bufo superciliari* from Equatorial Africa assumes any position in which it happens to be.

The reader will presently note how very like is this behavior of the giant African toad to that displayed by the lowly walking stick.

Curiously, not all individuals of a given species act alike, although we are accustomed to thinking of reptiles and amphibia as ex-

Playin' possum. Photograph by Underwood & Underwood.

hibiting only a modicum of individuality; but that is because we do not know individuals of those classes intimately enough. That unschooled persons see similarity in behavior of the opossum and lower forms is illustrated by the following quotation from Mrs. Cecile Hulse Matchat's interesting book *Suwannee River:*

> A harmless spreading adder, locally known as 'possum, puts on such a ferocious appearance when disturbed that the swampers firmly believe it to be poisonous. But call " 'possum's" bluff and it flops over and plays dead. Withdraw a few steps and it turns on its belly and hastens to crawl out of sight; make a startling noise and it plays dead again.

In the animal scale it is a far cry from snake to opossum, but how alike the behavior. The resemblance is so striking, as noted in the last quotation, that the natives transfer the name possum without reference to erudite anatomy or the niceties of animal classification. It is interesting to note that, according to Morris Steggerda, the Mayan Indians apply their word for opossum, namely *och,* to a patient bedridden with malarial fever.

Among the vertebrates some of the best dissimulators are the protectively colored ones. Flush a mother quail leading her young brood out foraging and she will suddenly emit a warning cry and fly away in a manner inviting pursuit, while the chicks "freeze" on the spot and, by virtue of their color, blend unseen with the dry leaves and bark of the woodland.

All of the creatures so far mentioned are

65

"high" in the hierarchy of animal life compared with invertebrates, such as Crustacea, spiders, and insects; yet death-feigning is to be observed in the last in its most exquisite expression. If you touch the leaf of a potato plant infested with potato beetles, in the twinkling of an eye they roll off and lie still for a variable length of time. It is the slow-moving insects, however, that are the most constant and reliable performers; those, on the other hand, better adapted to escape with more agile legs or wings tend to save themselves through their speed. Leaflike locusts and grasshoppers and the bizarre walking sticks remain '"frozen" for hours at a time, especially in daylight, when any movement on their part subjects them to detection by birds, as has been abundantly demonstrated by experiment.

In his well-known *Naturalist in Nicaragua*, Thomas Belt describes this self-protective behavior of a green leaflike locust in relation to invading hordes of the driver ant Eciton. These ferocious and formidable ants go on periodic raids, advancing in organized armies that leave nothing alive that has been too slow to escape from their path. Insects that attempt to escape by flight also fall into great danger, for birds that accompany the ants are ever on the lookout for any insect in motion. But Belt's leaf-mimicking locust stood immobile amongst a host of ants, many of which ran over its legs oblivious of the food so near at hand. So fixed was its instinctive behavior that Belt could pick it up and replace it among the ants, where it remained immobile as before.

That death-feigning is widespread in nature is evident; but descriptions of behavioral peculiarities do not serve as an explanation of them. It is characteristic of an unscientific and uncritical treatment of any subject that descriptive terms are substituted for explanations; the simulation–of death—playing possum—is a field peculiarly encumbered with such short cuts to mental satisfaction.

The terms for death-feigning are many and may be classified under several headings. At the least scientific level most of the terms are synonyms. There are the popular expression "playing dead" and the more sophisticated "counterfeiting death." The early naturalists, including Linnaeus, writing in Latin, used the expression *mortuum simulit*. An elegant modern coinage derived from the Latin is "letisimulation." A similar term derived from the Greek is "thanatosis." But as "death-feigning" implies that one is able to read the mind of the animal and to attribute to it conscious purpose, we must look upon such expressions merely as handy figures of speech that explain nothing.

Another category of names shows vague attempts to somehow correlate the terms with actual observations. Such are "freezing" or "immobilization reflex." Then there are a number of descriptive words that aim at being still more specific. The observed tetanic contractions of the muscles in death-feigning have provoked the use of "tonic immobility" and the German *Starrkrampfreflex*. Some speak of "hypnosis," suggesting the possible mental basis for the observed behavior. "Akinesia," which implies that the animal is powerless, is best in line with the thesis to be developed in this chapter. All of these makeshift terms merely define areas of ignorance and are not scientifically more satisfactory than the Negro concept quoted by Ernest Thompson Seton: "lay low and say nuffin'."

Numerous naturalists have emphasized the usefulness of this faculty: animals react that way instinctively, unlearnedly, because they are enabled thereby to escape danger. Those individuals that escape are, by and large, the ones that live to reproduce the race and so, by natural selection, the habit is perpetuated and perfected. There is ample experimental proof that certain organisms are gobbled up by their enemies when they move, whereas they are passed by unharmed if they remain motionless. The walking stick is a good example. Confine it in a cage with a bird and you will find that the instant the insect makes the slightest movement it is attacked. In bright light the insect is most vulnerable, and under such conditions it remains as still as the twig which it resembles. When the muscles are in tonic contraction, the insect may remain for long periods in the most astonishing postures.

Probably the earliest experimenters with tonic immobility were the magicians of the East. Motion pictures have demonstrated the art of the cobra-taming Hindu. The explanation is simple enough. If the serpent in its threatening attitude be deftly caught behind the head and gently pressed, it becomes stiff and will remain so for a considerable time. Moses made use of the trick in order to impress Pharoah:

And the Lord said unto him, What is that in thine hand? And he said, A rod. And He said, Cast it on the ground. And he cast it on the ground, and it became a serpent; and Moses fled from before it. And the Lord said unto Moses, Put forth thine hand, and take it by the tail. And he put forth his hand, and caught it, and it became a rod in his hand.—Exodus 4:2–5

Coming down to more recent times, we may cite one Daniel Schwerter, who in 1636 published a book of parlor games and recreational exercises, among which the one concerning the technique of hypnotizing the hen has become famous. The method was exploited by that versatile forerunner of writers of popular science, Father Athanasius Kircher. In 1646 this worthy published a book in which he dubbed Schwerter's experiment with the hen *experimentum mirabile imaginatione gallinae* and gave direc-

Young opossum "playing possum" when approached by a raccoon. Photograph by Underwood & Underwood.

67

tions for its performance. You tie the hen's legs with a ribbon, lay her on a table, and draw a chalk line in a diagonal direction from one eye to the other. Kircher simplified the experiment by suggesting that it is not necessary to make an actual line on the table as Schwerter required—a line in mid-air will suffice, for the hen will "imagine" the line and therefore consider herself tied down, and will remain quiet even though the ribbon that first bound her be removed.

Strangely enough the phenomenon was not scientifically investigated until Czermak took up the problem in 1873, although the practice of "magic" had been under scrutiny a century earlier by a Royal French Commission of which our own Benjamin Franklin was a member. Czermak quickly disposed of the chalk-line idea and also the hen's fertile imagination, which he transferred to the wishful thinking of Kircher himself.

The secret of this performance, we know today, is the ease with which hens and roosters may be "hypnotized." It is necessary only to lay the animal on its back and to hold it gently but firmly until the muscles gradually relax as you loosen your hold. A rotating turntable is said to hasten the process. Years ago I observed a little girl who, forsaking her inanimate dolls, made playmates of Rhode Island Red hens and roosters. She would "hypnotize" the birds, place them in her doll carriage, and roll them around for hours. This sight would have provoked dire whisperings among the witch-burners of Cotton Mather's day.

Just as amusing is the hoax played in his youth by the famous entomologist Favre and his companions when the boys caught an absent farmer's barnyard fowl and tucked their heads under their wings, where they remained until the farmer returned and found his barnyard uncannily quiet.

Guinea pigs likewise lend themselves to immobilization experiments. With one quick, smooth movement the subject is inverted

Frog in state of tonic immobility.

from prone to supine position, preferably in an apparatus made for this purpose. It was reported in *Science* (Liebman, July 8, 1948) that it is possible to train guinea pigs to prolonged hypnosis, so that some, like the walking stick, will remain in most uncomfortable stances for as long as two hours.

Lizards are notoriously easy to put under the "spell," as many a boy can testify. Here again the subject is turned over on its back and—so the traditional directions prescribe—the animal is stroked on its chest. This gives the demonstration a more professional air, though the stroking is not essential. However, many a Tom Sawyer who conditions his wild bass to come to the water's edge to have its chin tickled might well insist on such a procedure.

Frogs, too, lend themselves well to experimentation in this field and are subject to the same techniques as the other species mentioned.

Spectacular performances may be elicited experimentally in insects and other arthropods. The slender water strider Neides may be put into the cataleptic state by a light tap on the thorax. The leaf-mimicking Phyllium will under proper conditions maintain the most bizarre stances for hours, in response to either mechanical stimuli or intense light. That both flexor and extensor muscles are involved is well shown in the walking stick's standing on its head and especially by its serving as a "cataleptic bridge."

Aside from the stiffening of the body due to a considerable if not maximal increase in muscular tone, little is known of what goes on in the bodies of these creatures. In the rabbit and the guinea pig the pulse and respiration are more rapid. Since the position assumed is that of an animal attempting to right itself, it is likely that the higher nerve centers are involved. On the other hand, one may recall the behavior of frogs and toads decapitated while mating; in this condition the nuptial embrace of the brainless male persists for hours or even days once the muscles are "set" in the mating act. Normally, the male relaxes his hold on the female in response to the characteristic croak which she emits when she has finished the deposition of eggs.

If we compare our experimental animals induced to assume the catatonic state with wild animals in a similar state, as when the opossum plays possum, we see little difference. The reflexes are inhibited, the muscles taut, so that the animal is stiff or at least like soft wax that "stays put."

Many naturalists who have reflected on this problem believe that this state may be explained as a symptom of fear. Fear is an emotion with which we are acquainted by introspection; and since our actions when we are frightened mirror those of animals in similar situations, we feel that we are on safe ground in attributing death-feigning and other forms of catalepsy to fear or fright.

> . . . whilst they, distill'd
> Almost to a jelly with the act of fear,
> Stand dumb, and speak not to him.

On closer analysis, however, the explanation seems inadequate. In man fear is not essential to the cataleptic state, since this may be induced by hypnosis. Moreover, there are few signs of fear in the experimental animals brought into exaggerated and continuous bodily tonus by turning or stroking. In most cases the reactions to a sudden stimulus are too rapid to be controlled by conscious emotions. For instance, in a near-collision while driving an automobile, you are a half-mile down the road before your adrenaline begins to act, and then it is too late for the resulting fear to be of any use.

Perhaps we may come a little closer to an analysis of the phenomenon we are considering by examining in detail the reactions of the potato beetle. It sits on the leaf of the plant munching away. Touch one of the leaves ever so lightly and the beetle loses its grip and drops like a pebble. The reaction is purposive in that a useful end is attained; but who would say that it is due to reflection and cogitation? The insect falls into the most cataleptic fit imaginable. A tiny fraction of a second changes an active living being into a creature as helpless as the clod of dirt beside which it lies.

The reaction is, I think, mediated by the nervous system and is the result of changes in the brain and ventral ganglia. As Hudson Hoagland observed long ago, the changes come on explosively, but pass off gradually. One is tempted to assume that in the nerve centers there are certain labile substances which are harmless in themselves but which serve as precursors to substances that paralyze. The stimulus of a touch or a beam of light causes nerve impulses which act as percussion caps to set off the charge. The resulting new substances so stimulate the motor nerve fibers that the muscles, all of them, on both sides of the joints, contract, causing the stiffening of the limbs. After a period of time the paralyzed animal recovers, as a result, perhaps, of the diffusion of the paralyzing substances out of the nerve cells or their destruction by enzymes. Analogous compounds that function continuously on a low level, at times on a pathological level, in our own bodies are epinephrine, acetylcholine, and pituitrin. The theory is highly mechanistic. It follows, if the reasoning is correct, that the animal involved cannot help itself any more than the leaf of the sensitive plant can help closing when touched. The opossum faints because he cannot help doing so; therefore there are no real grounds for speaking of him as a "sly, cunning rascal" or an "adroit cheat."

Some may insist that we should except the fox, the opossum, the bird, and, above all, man from the operation of so mechanistic a process, and confine the application of the theory to the insects and other lowly forms that seem perfectly helpless in the throes of the cataleptic fit. Yet the more I see of animals that simulate death, the more I doubt that there are fundamental differences among species. As the great Harvard physiologist Walter B. Cannon first proved, even human beings, when frightened or angry, are under the sway of chemical substances in the blood and the nervous system.

Perhaps anything that is, is useful. In a state of nature, death-feigning is of undoubted value. This is more readily apparent and more susceptible of experimental proof in the lower than in the higher animals such as the opossum.

Ample evidence has been presented to show that playin' possum is not the exclusive property of the opossum tribe. While opossums are regarded as star performers in death-feigning, not all individuals of the race will play the role. Enders says that Metachirus, a courageous fighter, seldom "swoons with terror," and Davis mentions the same for *Didelphis marsupialis* of Brazil. My own experience with a thousand Virginia opossums in captivity has shown that they soon lose the faculty, greeting an intruder with open jaws when he opens the door of their cage. Only occasionally does one find an individual that is accommodating enough to perform for the curious visitor in the classical fashion.

It must have been a good performer which fooled Audubon, who recorded in his diary: "Capt C Bought an Opossum, Dash after having broke I thought all its bones left it—it was thrown over Board as if dead, yet the moment it toucht the Watter he swam for the Boats."

This chapter appeared in the January, 1950, number of the *Scientific American* and, with slight changes, is here reprinted by permission.

10

Opossum Embryology in Pictures

WHEN THIS COUNTRY was in its teens and science in its infancy, Dr. Benjamin Smith Barton, professor of materia medica and various other branches of the natural sciences at the University of Pennsylvania, contributed much to our knowledge of the opossum. A half-century after Barton, Dr. John D. Godman in his *American Natural History* (1846) summed up opossum lore in this way:

Centuries have elapsed since this species was first observed by European naturalists, and it has long been a frequent theme of admiration and discussion to those in America, yet it is still considered as a sort of anomaly among animals, and the peculiarities of its sexual intercourse, gestation, and parturition, are to this day involved in profound obscurity. Perhaps nothing can more clearly demonstrate the impatience of the human mind, and the reluctance with which men yield to the hard necessity of carefully observing the operations of nature, than the history of this animal. Volumes of facts and conjectures have been written on the subject, in which the proportion of conjecture to fact has been as a thousand to one, and the difficulties still remain to be surmounted. The animal is among the most common within our borders, and is annually killed or captured in large numbers; faithful investigations into the habits of a few individuals would be sufficient to settle all doubts forever, and yet these still remain to be made. Very full and interesting observations have been made at almost every other period; but the great question how the helpless offspring, weighing scarcely a grain, are conveyed into the external pouch and attached to the teats of the mother, has never been properly answered.

How the marsupial young reach the pouch was the enigma that most naturalists wanted solved above all else; but the distinguished French embryologist Coste, contemporary of John Godman, was especially intrigued to learn how the marsupial embryo developed in the uterus. He complained:

We are totally ignorant of the most general processes that take place in the uterus of marsupials during the development of the egg. One studies in vain the works of *voyageurs* or of savants who have written on the generation of the Didelphidae. This hiatus in our knowledge would without doubt disappear if one would collect, in the regions where they are indigenous, a sufficient number of the animals of this genus, mate them, and sacrifice them at given periods after impregnation. In the meantime we shall still remain in the realm of conjecture.

The hope expressed by Coste has been realized, probably in greater detail than he imagined. The story of the development of the opossum egg and embryo can be read, however, only in technical journals or in a book by Dr. Edward McCrady, Jr., written for the professional embryologist. The facts interred in such literature have little chance of reaching the general reader, especially in the South, where books are still relatively scarce. In this section many still believe, and often vehemently insist, that baby opossums are blown into the pouch out of the mother's nostrils. To help dispel this bizarre bit of folklore and to give photographic evidence that the opossum's eggs and embryos do actually develop within the uteri of the mother, as in all mammals, a liberal number of drawings and photographs are spread before the reader in the following pages.

The first attempt to fill the hiatus mentioned by Coste was not made by one "living where opossums abound," but by Professor Selenka, of Würzburg, Germany, who published an impressive volume descriptive of a few eggs and numerous embryos taken from a shipment of one hundred Virginia opossums imported from the United States.

Nothing more was done on marsupial development until 1911, when J. P. Hill, of London, published a monograph on eggs of the "native cat," an Australian marsupial, thus anticipating us in America by a few years.

In 1913 I caught my first opossums, not for food or merely for the fun of the chase, but to collect from them eggs and embryos about which I was curious. This egg hunt proved fabulously easy, for on the average twenty-two eggs may be recovered from a fertile female at a single breeding. My studies were based on nearly two thousand eggs and embryos comprising every stage of development. Pictures, mostly photographs, were published of about six hundred specimens of the three or four thousand collected. Many were photographed in the living state, fresh from the uterus.

Once and for all time the opossum has been freed of the stigma of being an utterly unorthodox mammal. It must now be conceded that the opossum has its babies like any other mammal, albeit a bit prematurely.

The opossum egg has, in miniature, all the features of a hen's egg except the hard outer shell. If you split open a hard-boiled egg of the domestic hen, you will note on the outside the calcareous shell and under this a thin but rather tough membrane, the shell membrane. The bulk of the egg consists of egg white, with the yolk in the center. The yolk, which is the egg proper since it comes from the ovary, comprises one-fourth of the egg volume; i.e., the yolk and albumen are to each other as one to three.

Transitional between the large food-laden eggs of birds and the minute eggs of the higher mammals are those of the platypus. The most primitive of all mammals, the platypus actually lays eggs and incubates them. They measure only about 6.5 mm., or a quarter of an inch, in diameter and, like snake and lizard eggs, have a shell membrane, egg white, and yolk. The opossum egg, also, has these parts, as the reader may assure himself by fingering through the illustrations presented in this chapter. But the opossum egg does not contain enough food material to nourish the embryo, which therefore has to live on substances taken from the mother through the wall of the uterus.

The opossum egg, with full complement of albumen and shell membrane, measures at most 0.75 mm., or about one thirty-second of an inch, in diameter. The essential part, that which will form the embryo, is the yolk or true egg in the center. This is usually less than 0.135 mm. in diameter (one one-hundred-eightieth of an inch); hence the albumen constitutes two hundred times the volume of the tiny ovum in the center. So it figures out that a hen's egg, which has a volume of 17,100 cu. mm., would hold about 10,000 opossum eggs, egg white and all. But the yolk, which is one-fourth of the entire hen's egg, if hollow would hold about 4,000,000 opossum yolks—and, incidentally, about the same number of human eggs, for the human egg and the opossum egg yolk have about the same dimensions. To gain an idea of the minuteness of a mammalian egg, try this: scatter on a piece of black paper a pinch of fine sea sand; the very smallest grain that you can see with the

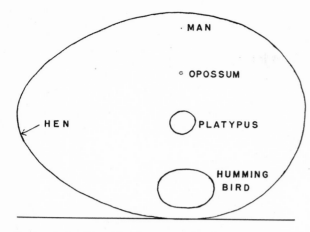

Eggs of the hen, the hummingbird, the platypus, the opossum, and man, drawn approximately natural size.

unaided eye is of the order of magnitude of a human egg or an opossum yolk.

In the drawings on pages 74 and 75, nearly seven days of development are covered. First there is the naked ovum or yolk as it comes from the ovary. Within twenty-four hours it becomes covered with albumen and the shell membrane. At the end of the seven-day period the egg has reached the stage of a hollow vesicle lined with three cell layers. In this there is, as yet, only a tiny rudiment of the embryo present, although half of the intra-uterine life has already passed. In six more days the embryos have to be ready for birth and their precarious trip to the pouch. The transition from delicate vesicle smaller than a pinhead to newborn opossum requires only six days. From these data we may calculate the total period of gestation from mating to birth at just about twelve days and eighteen hours.

What further evidence is there that this estimate is correct?

The span of pregnancy in the opossum, based on observed matings and births, was approximated very early. In 1783 the Count d'Aboville, who spent some years in America, determined the period to be fourteen days. Dr. Meigs arrived at the same figure. Dr. Michel might have corroborated these find-

ings exactly if his medical practice had not prevented his looking for the embryos in the pouch before the sixteenth day after the observed mating. D'Aboville's data were not known to Barton or to Rengger, whose estimates ranged from twenty-two to twenty-six days.

Very precise was Selenka's calculation of the period of gestation in the opossum, as was also my own, for we both found young in the pouch thirteen days after mating. Mc-Crady reduced this time to the more exact twelve days and eighteen or nineteen hours. Selenka and I also found embryos still in the uterus but apparently ready for birth twelve days and eighteen hours after a fertile mating.

In addition to these figures I have collected many data of a different sort. As the opossum has two uteri, it was easy to remove one of them by aseptic surgery and to determine the stage of development of the eggs contained therein, leaving the other uterus to incubate the remainder for a precalculated period of time.

The opossum provides no elaborate placenta for any extended nourishment of the embryos; hence they cannot tarry long in the uterus. The blood capillaries of the embryos simply lie close to those of the maternal circulation, and what nourishment the embryos get, passes from mother to fetus. The opossum fetuses remain the shortest time of all mammals. The golden Syrian hamster stays sixteen days, rats and mice twenty-one. But the opossum is born so prematurely and hence so small that an entire litter of twenty individuals can fit into a teaspoon. Is it any wonder, then, that opossum newborn have been called "veritable abortions"?

The story of the development of the opossum is presented painlessly in the form of pictures. The photographs afford the reader some faint idea of the beauty of the crystal-clear spheres which time and again I saw roll into warm salt solution as they were washed from the freshly opened uterus.

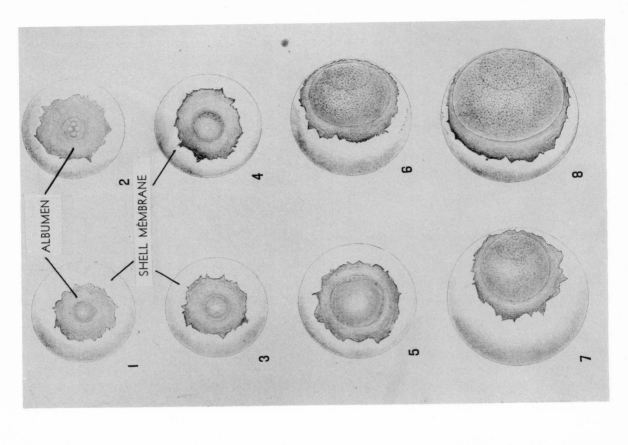

ALBUMEN

SHELL MEMBRANE

1 2 3 4 5 6 7 8

OPOSSUM EGGS (right)

Sketches of opossum eggs drawn from nature. Six days of development are represented in Figures 1 to 8.

Figure 1. The undivided true egg is in the exact center of the egg white, or albumen. At this stage the egg is still in the oviduct.

Figure 2. A four-celled egg from the uterus (at 36 hours).

Figure 3. At three and one-half days there are about forty cells, arranged in the form of a hollow sphere. All mammals, including man, pass through a similar stage.

Figures 4 and 5. The vesicle enlarges (four and four and one-half days respectively). At one pole (to the right in the drawings) cells destined to form the embryo congregate and multiply rapidly.

Figures 6, 7, and 8. The cells that will make the embryo (disc at right) are more active than the cells of the nonformative portion, hence require more food material, the albumen. This part of the vesicle therefore approaches closer to the shell membrane.

MICROSCOPIC SECTIONS (below)

Drawings of microscopic sections of twenty-two opossum eggs. These cover seven days of development. The sections were cut one five-thousandth of an inch in thickness. Thus the eggs shown in Figures 2, 3, and 4, scarcely visible to the naked eye, made twenty to thirty slices each.

Figure 1. The ripe egg still in the ovary.

Figures 2 to 6. Eggs from the oviduct. The egg shown in Figure 5 has acquired only a thin layer of albumen; the one in Figure 6, its full complement and the shell membrane.

At "PB," polar body containing eleven chromosomes cast off by the egg. At "CH," eleven chromosomes retained by the egg. What is the meaning of this behavior of the egg cell?

The chromosomes are the bearers of hereditary characteristics handed down from parents to offspring. When the male cell or sperm fertilizes the egg, it brings in eleven chromosomes as the father's contribution to the heredity of the offspring. With the entrance of the sperm into the egg the normal number of chromosomes characteristic of the opossum, twenty-two, is restored and the new individual is started on its way to develop. All of the future billions of cells will each have twenty-two chromosomes. In man and monkeys the number is two times twenty-four, or forty-eight.

Figure 6. One-celled egg.

Figure 7. Two-celled egg (24 hours).

Figure 8. Four-celled egg (36 hours).

Figure 9. Sixteen-celled egg (48 hours).

Figure 10. Tiny vesicle of about forty cells (84–90 hours). Compare with Figure 3 in the preceding plate.

Figures 12 to 17 should be compared with sketches in the preceding plate as follows: 12 with 4, 13 and 14 with 5, 16 with 6, 15 with 7, and 17 and 18 with 8.

Figures 18 and 20 have cells arranged in two layers; in Figures 21 and 22 a third layer of cells has grown between the first two. From these three "germ layers" come all the organs of the animal's body.

The egg of Figure 22 has (at the left) the first rudiment of the embryo, which in only five and three-fourths days will be delivered into the world.

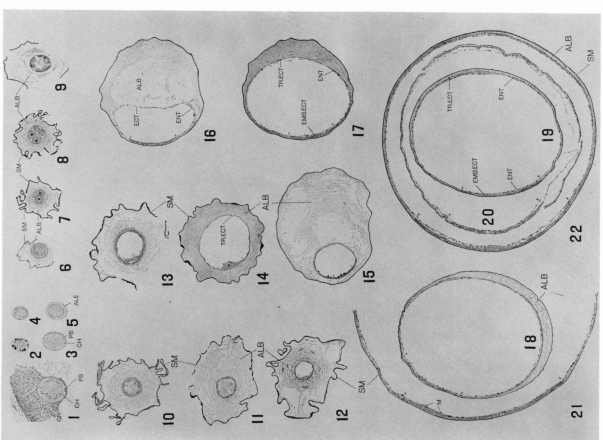

75

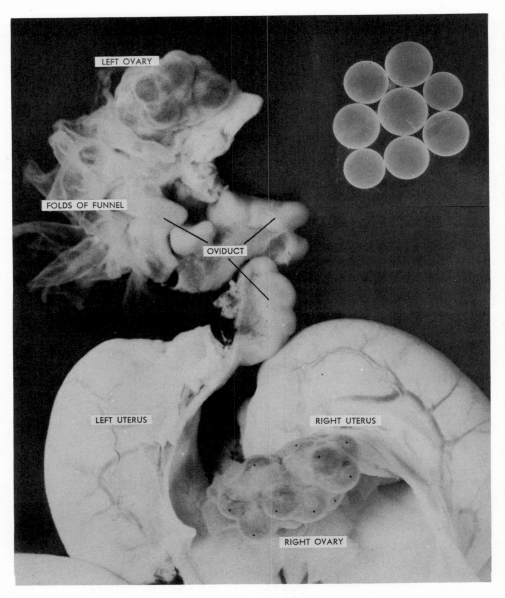

Uteri, oviduct (egg tube), and ovaries of the opossum. The gauzy folds of the oviduct's funnel normally envelop the ovaries. These are, at the stage shown, made up of vesicles called Graafian follicles filled with crystal-clear fluid. At eight days of development the opossum eggs are similar liquid-filled vesicles in the uterus (upper right). When, in 1668, De Graaf observed the same phenomena in the rabbit, he decided that the ovarian follicles constituted the actual eggs for which he had been searching in the ovary. How these got into the uterus through the needle-thin passageway of the oviduct he did not explain. It was not until 1827 that Von Baer found the true mammalian egg to be a tiny speck of protoplasm of near-microscopic size within the ovarian follicle. From the follicles the eggs are washed out at the right instant, are caught in the delicate folds of the funnel, and are passed through the oviduct to the uterus, where they are nourished until the time of birth.

The dots placed on the individual Graafian follicles of the right ovary are of about the size of the true eggs.

	1 Days	2	3	4	5	6	7	8	9	10	11	12	
190													
Selenka's Cases. (1887) →					◯	◯	◯	◉	⑧				→
134									→				13
314			→⊙						→				
114				→?					→				
298						→⊙			◉				
838							→◯						
343							→◯						
194					→◎								
306		⊙						→◯ ----360----		→			
299		⊞				→◯							
203		⊞		→⊙									
173		⊞	→⊙										
320		⊞						→◉					
293		⊞			→◯ ----585----				→				

Chart illustrating methods of calculating the period of gestation in the opossum: (1) the simplest, by determining the interval of time between an observed fertile mating and birth, as illustrated by Selenka's one case and our No. 190; (2) by noting the time interval between the stage of development attained by the embryos in one uterus of a given female and the stage attained some days and hours later by the embryos in the other uterus. In seven cases these intervals could be added to the period of time between the observed copulation and removal of the earlier stage.

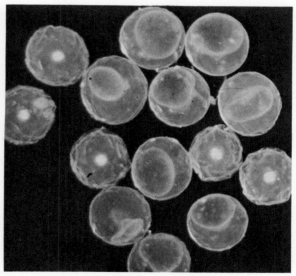

Left: litter of sixteen eggs with undivided yolks; three of the eggs are double-yolked, a phenomenon not rare in hens' eggs. Right: fourteen eggs, five days older than the litter shown at left; five eggs are unfertilized, and one or perhaps two of the nine vesicles are abnormal.

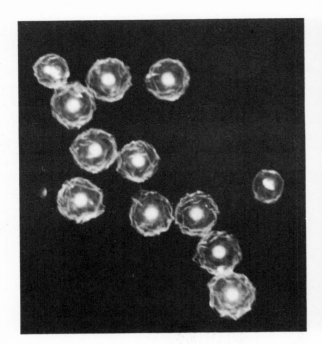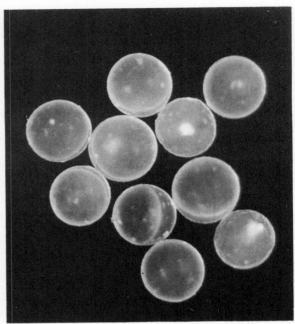

Left: litter of eggs in the four-celled stage (divisions of the yolk not apparent in the living egg). Right: sister eggs taken from the surviving uterus three and one-half days later.

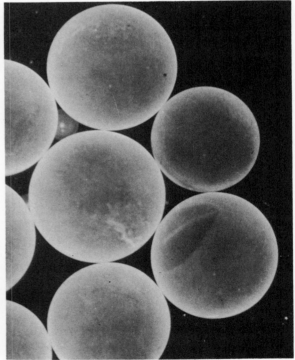

Left: batch of eggs in stage of small vesicles; the light areas mark the places where the embryo will form. Right: large vesicles, diameter 2.5 mm., age eight days; the streak on the pear-shaped dark area marks the site of origin of the embryo.

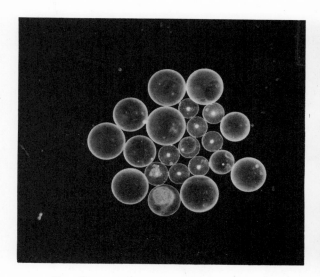 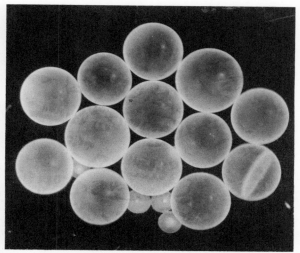

Two litters of eggs from the same animal separated by ten to twelve hours of development.

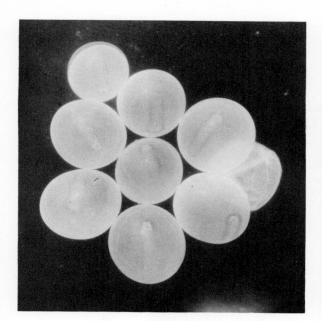 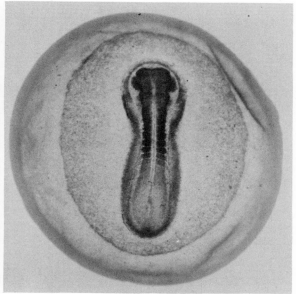

Eggs with embryos in the first third of the ninth day. Left: nine eggs, one collapsed, photographed in the living state by reflected light. Right: one of the eggs mounted in alcohol and photographed by transmitted light. The brain now consists of closed cavities; the streak in the center is the still-open spinal cord. Seven or eight pairs of somites can be made out; these will make muscle and connective tissue. In the pebbled area with sharply outlined outer edge, fetal blood vessels will soon form.

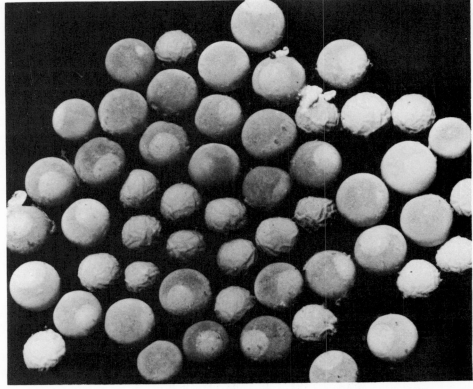

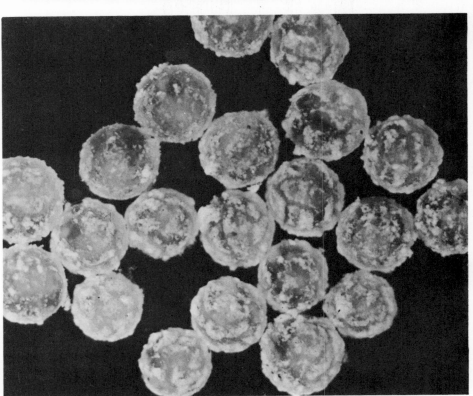

Left: a litter of twenty-one eggs, which is about the average number. These eggs, however, were not fertilized and were long dead and had become encrusted with proteinaceous matter from the uterus.

Right: fifty-four of a litter of fifty-six eggs; thirty-two had been fertilized, as proved by the development attained (note formative, i.e. embryonic, areas, which are lighter than the rest of the egg). This is the largest litter of spontaneously ovulated eggs ever found in any opossum at a single breeding. I have recorded, in addition, the following unusually large litters of eggs: 30, 33, 33, 36, 39, 39, 43, 44, 44, and 45.

Opossum vesicles of the eighth day of development. Left: photographed alive within the opened uterus. Right: the vesicles after being flushed out of the uterus into a dish of salt solution. The embryos are surrounded by areas where blood and blood vessels are to form. Actual diameter, just under three-eighths of an inch.

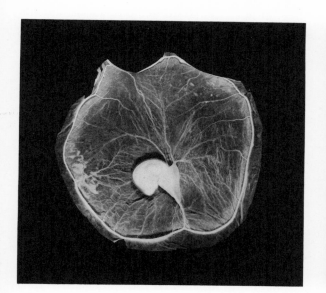
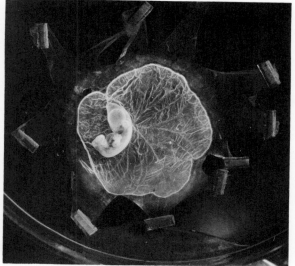

Left: embryo and its envelopes of the eleventh day, somewhat enlarged. Right: twelve hours later, actual size. Note precocious forelimbs, round allantois, and highly developed fetal blood vessels. The blood is gathered up by the stout marginal vein and returned to the embryo. It is by the vascular equipment that the embryo is enabled to gather food from and give off waste to the maternal blood vessels lining the uterus. Courtesy Chester H. Heuser and the Wistar Institute.

81

11

Birth of the Opossum

FOUR CENTURIES after the discovery of the first marsupial, the opossum, it has been finally established that opossums, kangaroos, and their relatives pass through a uterine gestation as do other mammals and, indeed, some of the lower viviparous vertebrates. The proofs have been overwhelmingly documented in the preceding chapter. Peculiar to marsupial mammals are the short gestation period, the consequent immaturity of the newborn young, and the subsequent long incubation in the pouch. Before discussing the age-old problem of the embryos' journey to the pouch, it seems appropriate to consider the manner in which the embryos pass down the birth passage, emerge all wet and bedraggled, and are set free by the mother for their initial and most precarious journey.

When parturition is imminent, the mother makes this known to the observer by her actions. She becomes restless. From time to time she sits up and pushes her muzzle into her pouch, "cleaning it," one is tempted to say. Going a step further, one credits her with a motive for this cleaning: readying the pouch for the reception of the "expected" young. Such a remark might be allowed to pass, but only figuratively. It is manifestly going too far to credit the opossum female with fore-thought and conscious purpose; it is sentimental and not scientific to go into ecstasies over the maternal foresight of Mother Opossum. Her behavior is worthy of admiration, but no more so than is any other of the countless adaptive mechanisms with which nature abounds.

To invoke blind instinct as accounting for the mother's remarkable behavior is as unscientific as to call it premeditated. To do so, moreover, is futile, for this begs the question and closes the door to further inquiry into possible physiological impulses underlying her acts. Discovery of some of the internal impulses in lower animals may well throw light on our own actions, many or perhaps most of which are now classed as instinctive.

We may ask first: What clue do we have concerning the internal factors that suddenly change the placidity of pregnancy into the uneasiness of parturition?

Common to all species of mammals, including man, when the female is about to give birth, contractions of the uterus begin to grow stronger and may reach the stage where they cause pain—labor pains. In the opossum the birth contractions are probably quite mild because of the minuteness of the fetuses to be expelled.

The cause of birth is unknown. It is be-

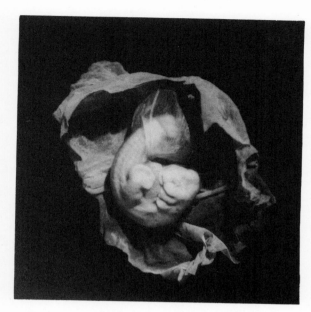

Opossum embryo in its envelopes. The outer envelope, the chorion, serves the embryo to make intimate contact with the wall of the uterus for the purpose of securing nourishment. Note the stout blood vessel running to the embryo. Enlarged four times.

lieved, however, that one portion of the pituitary gland situated at the base of the brain secretes into the blood stream at the proper time a chemical or hormone which whips the uterus into action. These uterine spasms, even when they are light, stimulate the female into the pattern of behavior characteristic of the species. This conclusion is justified by the following experiment.

Among the females which I was watching in my endeavors to witness the birth of the opossum, there was one that seemed favorable, for the hour of mating was known. This experimental subject was placed under observation at the calculated time. Her pouch was moist and oily; her mammary glands were enlarged as at the end of pregnancy; yet no babies came. When she was considerably overdue, I resorted to the obstetrician's drug for starting labor in women, namely, pituitrin (made from the pituitary gland mentioned above), and injected a large dose into the

opossum patient. Immediately she responded by licking the pouch, and this behavior continued for some time. Later it was found that she was not pregnant; yet she had behaved like a normal female about to expel matured fetuses.

We may inquire a bit further and ask why the female licks the pouch and not other parts of her body. Perhaps this localized attention is due to the swollen condition of the breasts. During the twelve and three-fourths days of pregnancy the mammae develop with great rapidity, for they must be ready to nourish the young immediately after birth. I have often followed the changes by feeling of the glands daily. Indeed, I learned to diagnose the stage of pregnancy with some degree of accuracy by simply palpating the glands in the pouch—the thicker the glands, the further the gestation was found to have progressed. At the time of birth the glands are quite swollen and would seem well able to offer at least some slight discomfort, hence the licking.

This licking of the pouch just before the birth of the young calls to mind a purely American legend concerning the mode of reproduction of the opossum. It is one of the most widespread traditional beliefs in the United States, especially in the South, and yet one of the most preposterous misapprehensions in the annals of folklore.

The legend affirms that opossums copulate through the nose and that after a period of time the products of conception, the tiny fetuses, are blown into the pouch. How this traditional belief arose is easy to figure out. The copulatory organ of the male is bifurcate, that is, provided with a double glans, corresponding to the double openings of the female's internal canals, structures unknown to the uninitiated. Since the nostrils are the only double openings visible externally, and since the pouch is often discovered to be filled with a squirming mass of pink fetuses soon after the female has busied herself with her nose in the pouch, the traditional belief arose as a fairly logical, albeit superficial, explanation of a mysterious phenomenon.

Somewhat similar is the European legend that has young born from the mouth of the dam. John Brickell brought this legend, among others, to America. Concerning the generation of "weesels" he says: "It is very strange what some Writers have said of the Generation and Conception of the Animal, who confidently assure us that they Ingender at the Ear and bring forth their Young at the Mouth."

The basic idea is old. Did not Pallas Athene issue from the head of Zeus?

Among the unfounded presumptions which the early writers passed on to their European public, avid for exciting tales from the New World, is one that has the female opossum, about to deliver her young, seek the depth of the forest "to hide from her worst enemy, man," or, according to another version, to avoid the male, supposedly eager to devour his delicate offspring. Zoologist Pennant incorporated this story in his book. But Rochefort, instead of calling Papa Possum a villain, endowed him with a pouch so that he could relieve the female in the care and feeding of the young. A similar degree of naïveté was exhibited by Robert Kerr, a member of the Royal College of Surgeons, a practitioner in the renowned medical center, Edinburgh, and incidentally a naturalist. Besides agreeing with Rochefort on the exchange of parents, he wrote in his *Animal Kingdom* that the female of the pouchless crab-eating opossum "brings forth four or five young ones at a litter, and having no pouch, deposits them in the hollow of trees." So at one extreme we are asked to believe in the double protection of duty-sharing parents, and at the other we are told that young so tiny that they are veritable fetuses are deserted by their mother. We read further in Kerr's famous book that opossum pouch young are so firmly attached to the nipples that it is impossible to remove them

without tearing their mouths; and yet, in agreement with Rochefort, we also read that the male and the female pass the young back and forth between them so that they may alternately nurse them. Throughout marsupial literature there are many conflicting ideas.

Let us return to the parturient opossum mother and consider some further characteristics of her maternal behavior.

It has been mentioned above that when the young opossum emerges into the world it brings with it its original swaddling clothes, the embryonic envelopes. These consist of a thin veil-like bag, the amnion, fitting close about the embryo, and the chorion with its blood vessels that come in close contact with the uterine wall of the mother for the absorption of food and the excretion of waste by way of the maternal blood stream. These bags are filled with fluid. As the fetus emerges with fluid and envelopes, it must be freed of them, especially of the fluid. The reason is that the surface tension of water is so strong that the fetus cannot with its own strength work its way out; hence, without maternal assistance it drowns, like the fly in a drop of water described by J. B. S. Haldane in his pleasant essay, "On Being of the Right Size."

These conditions recall a tragedy which once befell a litter of opossums born to an anesthetized mother lying under the drapery of my operating table. All of the embryos were dead when discovered a few minutes too late, drowned in their own amniotic fluid.

The licking act, again, is instinctive; not even the inexperienced mother needs to learn how to care for her first-born. But the stimulus to the licking act also seems to have a physiological basis or "drive." The fact is that all mammals give every evidence of thoroughly relishing the taste of amniotic fluid, and indeed the whole afterbirth. I have made motion pictures of monkeys eating the entire afterbirth, licking the baby dry, and lapping up the amniotic fluid down to the last drop. To all appearances, they do this because they

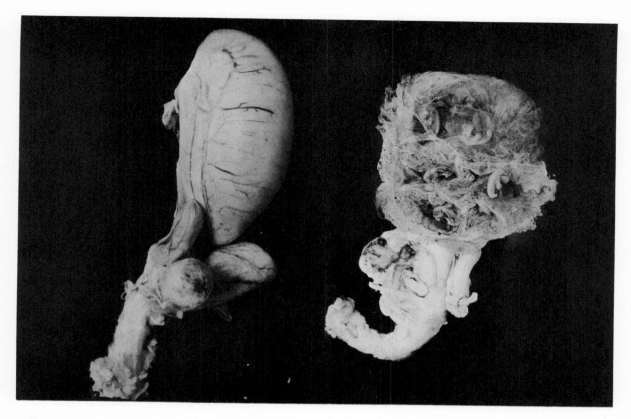

Pregnant uterus of the opossum. Left: the intact, surviving uterus of an animal from which the other uterus has previously been removed. Right: the uterus opened, showing embryos in their envelopes and the fluffy, soft character of the "basket they came in."

like it. A cow becomes a flesh-eating animal only when she has given birth to a calf. But when we ask why, we are met with another enigma, having just escaped from the preceding one.

After concluding that the parturient mother licks free the newborn young because she relishes the taste of the afterbirth, we now ask: "Are substances contained in the afterbirth of value to the mother nutritionally, hormonally, or otherwise?" Well, that's science—one question answered brings up a dozen more.

There is as yet no answer to the last question propounded, though numerous theories have been proposed. For most mammals it has been shown to be immaterial whether the mother eats the afterbirth or not, and this complicates the problem. With marsupials the circumstances are unique, and it is fairly clear that the mother must lap up the birth waters, not for a possible benefit to her own bodily economy, but to free the newborn fetuses of fluid and entangling envelopes. These are of little bulk in comparison with the elaborate placentae of higher mammals, or even those of certain sharks, snakes, and lizards. Marsupials represent a transition between the higher mammals on the one hand and on the other the monotremes—the duck-billed platypus (Ornithorhynchus) and the Australian anteater (Echidna)—which lay eggs and have no uterine gestation at all.

We must now retrace our steps to consider the passageways by which the opossum fetuses reach the exterior from the uterus. A

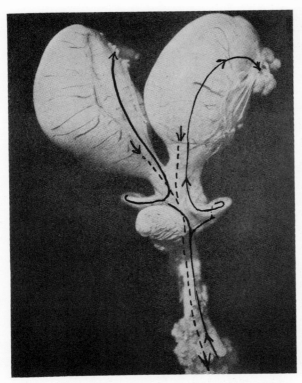

Female genital tract of the opossum. The uteri are swollen and contain embryos. The continuous line indicates the route the spermatozoa had to take (via the lateral vaginal canals) to reach the eggs and fertilize them. When the embryos are being delivered they short-circuit the lateral vaginal canals, breaking through by a new, temporary passage, as indicated by the dotted line.

reference to the accompanying figure will convince the reader that the normal route via the lateral vaginal canals is too circuitous.

The hydrostatics involved when there is pressure from above are such that the lateral vaginal canals would be actually closed off. The fact is that a new passage is forced through the loose connective tissue from the uterus to the vagina proper. This new birth passage characterizes all marsupials. I have been able to demonstrate this in the opossum on several occasions, but would probably have missed the point if my attention had not previously been called to it by the published work of J. P. Hill on the "native cat" and the bandicoot of Australia. But here again the great John Hunter, anatomist, experimenter, and physician to the King, anticipated us all by observations he made on the kangaroo 150 years ago. He, with his son-in-law Sir Everard Home, postulated that the young kangaroo "passes out by a particular opening which prior to gestation did not exist." The British student of comparative anatomy, Richard Owen, teacher and mentor of Charles Darwin, argued against Hunter's view, which has, however, been amply corroborated by Hill, Fletcher, and me.

This chapter constitutes a commingling of fact and fancy concerning a crucial stage in the life of the opossum. The facts are solidly incorporated in modern books, little read. Some fanciful beliefs have become traditional, having been carried from person to person by word of mouth through the centuries, and will doubtless persist for centuries to come.

12

Journey to the Pouch: Fancy

THE EARLY EXPLORERS who wrote about the opossum startled the world with the discovery of the marsupial gestation, and they never ceased to marvel at the minuteness and apparent helplessness of the young at birth. Little curiosity was at first expressed as to the origin of the young and the method by which they got into the pouch. The later groping of naturalists and popular writers for an explanation constitutes an incomparable example of the substitution of imagination, conjecture, and the beliefs of aboriginal peoples for simple and direct observation and experiment.

If attempts were actually made to determine how the opossum young reach the pouch, any use of the "look-see" method found Mother Opossum unco-operative. John Bachman said just a century ago: "There is great difficulty in deciding the question, whether the mother aids the young in finding the teats, in consequence of the impossibility of the spectator being able to know what she is actually doing when her nose is in the pouch."

Since it is so difficult to see just what is happening when a marsupial gives birth, early reports were based on deduction rather than on observation. When the Australian naturalist Dudley Le Souëf, for example,

tried to answer the question, How does the newborn kangaroo get into the mother's pouch? (*The Zoologist,* 1900; *Nature,* 1900), he figured it out in this way:

When the young one is ready to be born the mother sits down on the ground, resting on the upper portion of the base of her tail, and with that appendage resting level on the ground in front of her; she then holds her pouch open with her two fore-paws, and, as the helpless mite is born, it rests on the soft fur on the under side of the tail. The mother immediately transfers it to her pouch with her lips only, and evidently with great care attaches it to the nipple. The mouth of the young one is apparently only a round hole, and it as yet has no power of suction; but the nipple is of a peculiar shape, with point hard, and the mother is thereby enabled to insert it into the mouth of the young one. She then holds it in position while she pours the milk into the nipple, which thereby swells out and holds the young one on; but if, after once firmly attached, it is pulled off it cannot be replaced, even by the mother, for the end of the nipple now being flaccid instead of hard, cannot well be inserted into the mouth of the little one.

As it turned out Le Souëf was right about the posture of the parturient kangaroo, for she does sit up as described. The rest of the account he concocted out of circumstantial evidence. Later Le Souëf recognized his errors and published the necessary correction.

The majority of naturalists, I think, did accept the theory that the mother assists the young in some way, although dissenters protested that it would be no more astounding for the tiny bit of flesh to find the nipple by itself than for the clumsy mother to be able to place it there.

The well-informed German naturalist Rengger, who lived many years surrounded by Uruguayan opossums, expressed ignorance on the details of this stage of opossum life history but felt inclined to believe that the mother must help in some way, and he suggested that she probably used the clawless, opposable great toes to effect the transfer. He also had an alternative theory to be mentioned below. Others preferred to think that the opossum mother used her lips. Professor W. S. Barnard, for example, after admitting that the actual transfer of the embryo opossum from the uterus to the pouch had not been observed, went on to say: "But this must be done as with the kangaroo, where it is believed that the mother takes each newborn embryo between her lips and places it upon one of the nipples." The professor, obviously, did leave plenty of loopholes in his statement. That was back in 1875; but writers have continued with guesswork up to our own time. Eric Daglish, for instance, wrote in *The Life Story of Beasts:* "Immediately they are born, these tiny babies are taken up by the lips of the mother and are placed in a pouch on her abdomen." Perhaps he took his cue from Ernest Thompson Seton, who was not quite up to date in his *Life-Histories of Northern Animals,* in which he says that the mother opossum takes her half-dozen infants as fast as they are born and drops them into her pouch, where each seizes a teat and holds on.

A number of authors follow Le Souëf in crediting the opossum dam with the acuity of touch sufficiently delicate to place each embryo on its respective nipple, a procedure described by a writer in Hesse's and Doflein's well-known German zoology:

The young cannot reach the pouch by themselves but are grasped by the lips or the tongue of the mother and put in the pouch. Here each young one is placed on its teat. Once the nipple is grasped, the slit-shaped mouth becomes tubular. The young are then as firmly attached as if they were grown to the nipple.

John Bachman, usually most critical and conservative, came to about the same conclusion, namely, "that she shoved them into the pouch, and with her nose or tongue moved them to the vicinity of the teat."

Further speculation on the mystery of the opossum's birth produced an alternative theory on the part of biologists who knew some anatomy but not quite enough. It was assumed that the external orifice of the birth canal is brought into contact with the opening of the pouch and that the young, as it emerges, needs only to grasp a nipple to assure itself physical security. Rengger, still fumbling with ideas about the transfer, wrote: "How the young reach the pouch, however, I have never been able to observe. Perhaps as most naturalists believe, the two muscles that run from the marsupial bones to the anterior spine of the ilium are contracted at the time of birth, so that the young are shoved into the pouch through the impulse of birth itself." Catapulted, one is inclined to say.

Sastre is more specific: "The mother at the moment of birth bends her body so that one of her large teats enters the reproductive tract, where the young one adheres to the teat and is passed into the pouch." Fishing for the baby opossum, as it were.

About 1800 the German Reimerus, in a correspondence with Dr. Barton of Philadelphia, asked whether the opossum's vulva could approach sufficiently near the pouch to allow a direct deposition of the young into the pouch. Barton examined some opossums and convinced himself that such was actually the case: it was indeed possible. In his reply, however, he said that he was of the opinion that opossums are not born that way.

Quite recently W. Reid Blair, one-time director of the Bronx Zoo, expressed the notion that the kangaroo is capable of bringing the cloaca and the pouch close together at parturition, and he believed that "the young is normally expelled directly into the pouch." The great British anatomist Richard Owen, many decades before, had contended that the genital opening in the kangaroo cannot be brought to the pouch; but he also, for once, overreached himself by stating categorically that the mother "probably transports the young with her lips, using her claws to hold open the pouch." And so, through the years, guesses continued to substitute for direct observation.

Curiously enough, Australia's leading student of the egg-laying monotremes, Harry Burrell, thought it probable that the spiny anteater (Echidna) deposits her sizable eggs into the pouch by bending her supple body into a suitable position. Not that he witnessed the act; but he thought this logical, since echidna's paws, built to tear asunder ants' nests, were unsuited to picking up delicate eggs. Burrell's chief evidence, however, for the deposition of eggs directly from cloaca to pouch lay in his finding feces in the pouch containing the egg.

The two purely conjectural theories thus far discussed were the reasoned deductions of naturalists. They are sophisticated notions. Others, less reasonable, some almost bizarre, have been invented by primitive peoples: the American Indian and the natives of East Indian islands and Australia. The basic idea common to these theories is that marsupial embryos are bred and conceived in the pouch, not inside the abdomen as in other animals. Even professional naturalists at times accepted the natives' concepts with little hesitation.

The earliest reference I have found to this method of breeding originated in Virginia. Neither John Smith nor Thomas Ash bothered with the problem, and Ralph Hamor simply said that the mother "hides the young in her belly." But Thomas Harriot, writing up the natural history of the region of Sir Walter Raleigh's first colony, whose surveyor he was, said: "She is the wonder of all animals. The female doubtless breeds her young at her teats, for I have seen them stick fast thereto, when they have been no larger than raspberries." Doubtless—what volumes of doubt this much abused but still convenient word expresses! It is prima facie evidence that the author was guessing.

Subsequent to Harriot, writers on the natural history of Virginia and Carolina copied from him, perpetuating his interpretation. Robert Beverly wrote: "What is strangest of all is that in this membrane [pouch] the young are conceived and nourished without ever having been in the belly."

Lionel Wafer said the same. John Brickell, a physician who had apparently failed to read Tyson's description of the opossum's uterus, also argued for Harriot's opinion. Among the writers on the natural history of Virginia and Carolina the most scientific was Mark Catesby, whom I quote:

But what is more remarkable in this Creature and differing from all others, is its false Belly, which is formed by a Skin or Membrane (including its Dugs), which it opens and closes at Will. Though contrary to the Laws of Nature, nothing is more believed in America than that these Creatures are bred at the Teats by their Dams: but as it is apparent from a Dissection of them by Dr. Tyson, that their Structure is formed for Generation like that of other Animals, they must necessarily be bred and excluded the usual Way of other Quadrupeds; yet that which has given Cause to the Contrary Opinion is very wonderful, for I have many times seen the young ones just born, fixed and hanging to the Teats of their Dams.

It is clear from Catesby's statement that the legend was prevalent among the natives of eastern North America. This is corroborated by no less a zoologist than Geoffroy Saint-Hilaire. The latter got his information from a Frenchman who had accompanied Lafayette to America, had been taken prisoner by the Creek Indians, and had later become one of their chieftains.

While we have Catesby's word for the general acceptance of the theory in America, Dr. Benjamin Smith Barton, who knew well the Indians around Philadelphia a century and a half ago (Lenape and Delaware tribes, especially), claimed that the Indians knew that the pouch is not the true uterus—this in answer to a direct query from his Hamburg correspondent, Reimerus. Aside from Barton's and Catesby's statements I have no further data on the origin of the legend in North America; but it is significant that the selfsame idea arose among the Indians of the Amazon Valley and is a basic conviction of the aborigines of the East Indies and Australia.

After the British had smashed the Spanish Armada, north European nations began competing each for its share of the rich Far Eastern trade. In 1629 the shipwrecked Dutch sea captain Pelsaert, through accident, became the first to send back a report describing an Australian marsupial. To him it seemed certain that the wallaby's young were conceived in the pouch. He wrote:

Their manner of generation or procreation is exceedingly strange and highly worth observing. Below the belly the female carries a pouch, into which you may put your hand; inside this pouch are the nipples, and we have found that the young ones grow up in this pouch with the nipples in their mouths. We have seen some young ones lying there, which were only the size of a bean, though at the same time perfectly proportioned, so that it seems certain that they grow there out of the nipples of the mammae, from which they draw their food, until they are grown and able to walk.

Since Pelsaert made no direct contact with the "black fellows" of the mainland from whom he might have taken his cue, and since he probably had not read the Englishman Harriot, it is quite likely that the clever if erroneous concept originated with him.

Most of a litter of twenty newborn opossums in a teaspoon. Actual size.

Two other Dutchmen, Marcgrave and Piso, came to the same conclusion as Captain Pelsaert. These scientists were the first to study thoroughly the plants and animals of South America. They had ample opportunity for becoming well acquainted with several species of opossum. In 1638 they had accompanied Maurice of Nassau, appointed governor of the Netherlands' colony in America, to his headquarters at Mauritius, in Brazil, a possession later relinquished to the Portuguese. Piso served as physician to the Count, while Marcgrave, an astronomer and naturalist, came to study the southern constellations. For this purpose the Governor had an observatory built at the capital. In their individual as well as joint accounts of the natural history of the region, these pioneers concluded that opossums are not born but are conceived in the pouch. As Piso the physician put it: "The pouch is the uterus of the animal, it has no other, as I have determined by dissection. Into this pouch the semen is received and the young form therein." There we have it, in plain words. Evidently the mantle of Vesalius, the anatomist, had not fallen on Dr. Piso.

Neither of these two writers mentions the source of his ideas on marsupial gestation, but Du Tertre admits that he received the identical information from the Indians, though in general he prides himself on reporting only from direct observation—*esté témoin oculaire*. In this case, however, he said: "The pouch is invested with soft hair; the natives assure me that the young form there . . . and are nourished there, sucking eight small teats . . . and that the male, like the female, has the same and may alternately carry the young." Here are two glaring errors, at least one of which might easily have been checked with "ocular testimony."

The clear statements of Catesby and Du Tertre would seem to justify the conclusion that the concept of a purely marsupial gestation was the invention of the American Indian. In this belief the Indian was not alone, for on the opposite side of the earth other aborigines had arrived at a quite similar idea. In Amboina, one of the Dutch-owned Molucca Islands, Pastor Valentyn got the identical story from the natives under his charge. He cautiously confesses that he made no attempt to verify the statement. I translate freely the essential passage:

Reproduction in this animal [the filander] happens in a wonderful manner. It does not develop its young in the uterus enclosed in the belly, but possesses an outer belly or bursa . . . the lips of which are lined with fine hair. In it there is no opening into the belly. . . . Within the animal there is nothing that looks like a uterus [this all sounds strangely like Piso]. Whether the young grow on the teats like fruit on trees (which fall off when ripe) is a matter about which I cannot speak with certainty. But it is certain that they develop in the sac and were first discovered on the teats. Therefore the latter idea is the more probable, that they develop on the teats, for the bursa is tightly closed until the young are well grown. Also one finds naked young so tightly attached that if one pulls them off, bleeding follows.

This bit of nature lore which Valentyn learned from the Amboina natives, so far as the item of marsupial gestation is concerned, he might have picked up in Australia, where similar notions prevail in the folklore of the most primitive race of mankind. I am assured by J. Thomas Flynn, long a resident of Australia, that "the bushman almost universally believes that the young either grow on the teat or that the teat becomes everted, with a young one on the end of it. Some think that at birth a direct passage exists between the uterus and the pouch. In fact one author felt called upon to write a paper to show that no such passage exists." The late H. C. Raven, who traveled much in Australia for the American Museum of Natural History, also testified to the widespread distribution of the legend among the Arunta of Queensland.

The idea of marsupial gestation was not only widespread but it has endured. Ellis Troughton in his *Furred Animals of Australia* dilates on the tenacity with which the unscientific white settlers still cling to the false notion. "For many years," he says, "the argument has been waged by campfire, in the country bar and the city newspaper." A correspondent expressing his contempt for the findings of zoologists declared that he would stick to his opinion in spite of "Le Troughton and Co. and all your Pitt and George Street naturalists." In America, too, the tendency was to reject the findings of zoologists and to give credence to casual observation. A Texas frontiersman, James Buckner Barry, wrote:

Zooligy perhaps is nearer right than any other science, but it seems to me its teachers are behind on some variety of snakes as well as some varietys of animals, one of which is the opossom. Though science contradict my theory, I cant surrender an experimental truth, that the oposom delivers its young direct from the womb into the pocket through the old teet. The little fellows bringing a new teet from the womb in its mouth, which it never turns loose while it stays in the pocket. . . . The borning process is very slow, perhaps two weeks making their exit from the womb into the pocket. I have seen the little fellows when they were only half borned their hind parts in the pocket while their fore parts were yet in the womb. When they get too large for the pocket they are borned again into the wide world.

The manner of birth of the kangaroo was discussed by writers in *The Zoologist* (1889). Among them one Edward Bartlett, son of A. D. Bartlett, author of *Wild Animals in Captivity,* wrote: "I remember many lively conversations on that point with my father, who had the greatest opportunity [in the London Zoo] of knowing all about the breeding of animals and we came to the conclusion that the wormlike young [of the kangaroo] passed through a duct or canal in the mammary glands from the womb to the pouch, which would only be perceptible at the time of birth." Evidently Richard Owen, himself a frequenter of the London Zoo, was not exposed to the Bartlett views; at least Waterhouse, who had access to Owen's papers, does not mention the matter in his book on marsupials.

A sequel to the fanciful stories already written about the pouch came from the pen of the Frenchman Count Castellux, who said that "the long teat, after the pouch young is through with it, falls off after the manner of the umbilical cord."

Now if the old teats fall off, by what magic do the new teats appear when the need for them arises? This problem also has been "solved"—in a book. The trick was turned by Count d'Aboville. I quote from *Quadrupeds,* by Bewick, who took it from D'Aboville: "The paps are not disposed in regular order, as in other animals, but seem as if they are formed in those places where the embryos attach themselves to the mother." So simple to explain, and how convenient—a crop of new nipples wherever the newborn happen to settle and begin sucking.

Should we deride D'Aboville for not examining the opossum closer and searching for the nipples, since he had ample access to opossums in America? Certainly not; for even the professional anatomist Dr. Tyson, discoverer of the opossum uterus, had not found the nipples after due examination. He had searched with a preconceived notion of elongated nipples and, not suspecting how very tiny these structures are in the resting condition, he failed to find them.

In the absence of exact information, one theory followed upon another. In general there is nothing more useful than theory. It serves as a starting point from which to launch a program of careful research. Every theory must be thoroughly tested; and for this, observation is the best tool. How does the opossum young reach the pouch? The answer could come only from actually seeing the perilous journey consummated. From the welter of conjecture which I have disinterred from the world's literature of four centuries, we pass in the next two chapters to the solution of the mystery.

13

Journey to the Pouch: Fact

Naturalists of the more conservative sort early called attention to the "mystery" involved in the transfer of the newborn marsupial to the pouch. "By what method the opossum Dam, after Exclusion of the Young, fixes them to the Teats is a Secret yet unsolved," was honest Mark Catesby's comment two centuries ago. George Shaw wrote in his zoology textbook in 1800: "The method is one of those particulars in natural history which seems to have eluded investigators."

About the same time Professor Barton asserted less conservatively (for he did not know the answer either): "The young opossums, unformed and perfectly sightless as they are at this period, find their way to the teats by the power of an invariable, a determinate instinct, which may, surely, be considered as one of the most wonderful that is furnished us by the science of natural history." This, of course, tells us exactly nothing. In a footnote, however, he discredited the prevailing notion and contended that "the mother, with her paws, puts the young ones into the pouch. I shall show," he continued, "that the common opinion on the subject is entirely erroneous." I have been unable to find the promised proof in Barton's later writings.

Surprisingly enough, an author in the popu-

lar British *Elements of Natural History* (1801) also hit the nail on the head: "The young are exceedingly small, blind, naked, but they immediately creep into the pouch"—which was sheer clairvoyance for that day.

Early in the nineteenth century, Luis Berlandier, a Mexican member of the Texas-Mexico Boundary Commission, calling attention to the difficulties involved in witnessing the birth of the *tlaquatzin,* used these words:

It is only by analogy and the inspection of the organs, that naturalists are inclined to believe that the new generation is transferred to said pouch at a time we do not know; be it because of the size of the creatures, be it because the fertile female retires to the depth of the forest, or be it finally because Providence has desired to put forth the difficulties which man has for some time called "mysteries."

Towards the middle of the eighteenth century Buffon, in his monumental *L'Histoire naturelle, générale et particuliere,* made the suggestion that scientists study the opossum where it is indigenous and where specimens are available for research.

It took a century for Buffon's call to be answered. The first responder was the Virginian Charles D. Meigs, M.D., who proved to be right in what he wrote about the opossum, but oh how wrong in combating Dr. Oliver Wendell Holmes on the latter's theory of the infectious nature of childbed fever. As obstetrician to the opossum Dr. Meigs did very well. After trying for some years to come into possession of "that zoological gem," a pregnant opossum, he finally succeeded. He determined that the period of gestation was less than sixteen days, which approaches the truth; but he did not observe the birth. On the manner in which the young reaches the pouch he speculated a bit, but soon dismissed the topic thus: "How the foetus reaches the nipple after birth will remain a mystery."

About the same time Middleton Michel, also a physician, came very close to solving the problem, for on February 15, 1847, he was present at the birth of the opossum, about which he wrote:

The pregnant female was found standing on her hind legs; her body was much bent, and propped up against the corner of the cage; her muzzle in immediate contact with the cloacal opening, which was red, tumefied and distended; a young appeared at the opening, and was conveyed by the mother's mouth to the pouch, or, perhaps licked in, as her tongue seemed busily employed within, around and about the pouch.

Bachman was right when he wrote the next year on the difficulty of seeing just what is going on when the mother has her head in the way. While Dr. Michel missed the actual migration of the young, he did see the newly-born appear—the first person to witness any marsupial emerging into the world.

While Meigs and Michel were pursuing their hobby, natural history, John Bachman, a Lutheran pastor living in Charleston, South Carolina, was doing the same much more seriously. Specializing in mammals, Bachman prepared the text for *The Quadrupeds of North America* (1848), a book illustrated with the paintings of John James Audubon. This famous volume contains Bachman's astute observations on the opossum, and it brought up to date the existing knowledge about that animal. Bachman's motto was: "Nature, truth and no humbug. I will guess at nothing."

Seventy years passed before the problem of marsupial birth was again taken up—and this time solved—by my wife and me. Before we ventured to spy upon the accouchement of Dame Opossum, we had already gained some respect for the independence and spontaneous capabilities of the newborn. On several occasions we had experimented with them, gently removing them from the teats to which they had firmly attached themselves by means of their powerful tongues. What happened in one case is told in our notes: "Female No. 301 tied down and pouch opened. Young removed from teats, crawled about, moving hands alternately, as in swimming. They were able to crawl among hairs and find teats by their own efforts. One specimen, removed three times, found teat each time and three others found teats after wandering about." This experiment and others like it certainly argued strongly in favor of considerable independence on the part of these "embryos," a term that Meigs would have us abandon in favor of "breathing, sanguiferous, digesting pouch young."

These preliminary observations prepared the scene for the crucial case which we had the good fortune to witness. Here are the facts: Opossum No. 443 in our series was brought to the laboratory of the University of Texas on February 2, 1920, having been captured uninjured several nights before. She was a healthy female of medium size, and by palpation of her mammary glands we recognized her as pregnant and likely to give birth within a few days. We removed her to our home, where she was kept under close observation night and day. The animal was placed just outside a window in a cage illuminated within by a red electric light, which arrangement proved least disturbing to the animal, particularly since she was insulated against noises from within the room. The sight of persons moving about in the room caused little response on her part, but slight noises near the cage startled her greatly.

94

At 10:30 P.M., on February 6, the animal became restless and soon began cleaning out the pouch. This she did about four times. Then began a short series of spasmodic contractions of the abdominal wall, after which she came to a sitting posture with legs extended. She then bent her body forward and licked the vulva; however, her position at this time was such that we could not see the embryos, which very likely passed into the pouch with the first licking of the genital opening. We therefore went to the outside, where we could plainly hear her lap up the chorionic fluid; then suddenly a tiny bit of flesh appeared at the vulva and scampered on over the entanglement of hair into the pouch to join the other fetuses which now could be seen to have made the trip without our having been able to observe them. Unerringly the embryo traveled by its own efforts. Without any assistance on the mother's part, other than to free it of liquid on its first emergence into the world, this twelve-and-three-quarter-day-old embryo, in appearance more like a worm than a mammal, is able, immediately upon its release from its liquid medium, to crawl a full three inches over difficult terrain. Indeed, it can do more: after it has arrived at the pouch, it is able to find the nipple amid a forest of hair. This it must find or perish.

Fortunately these observations, made at Austin, Texas, found rather prompt verification. Edward McCrady, working at the Wistar Institute of Anatomy and Biology in Philadelphia (adjoining the University of Pennsylvania, where Dr. Barton had studied opossums a century and a half before), gave the following vivid description of opossum fetuses making their way to the pouch and, what is more, finding and taking hold of the nipple:

When the young enters the pouch he finds himself in a mass of tangled, curly hairs among which he must locate one of the thirteen available, tiny mammary nipples—about the size of the head of a common straight pin. . . . Perhaps the most amazing thing that he does is that he succeeds in this search; but once in the pouch, he is almost certain to do so. . . . The head is moved in wide excursions to right and left, and when the snout finally touches the soft, moist, and warm nipple, the wandering stops and the young promptly sucks the nipple into its mouth.

Further corroboration of our observations on the independent ability of the newborn to reach the pouch was published by L. M. Dickerson, who had taken a female that was in labor when removed from a trap. He saw the young crawl as we had described the act (*Science*, August 3, 1928).

The best job yet made, however, of observing the birth of the opossum must be credited to Harold C. Reynolds, whose ecological studies have already been mentioned. This investigator, working at the Museum of Vertebrate Zoology of the University of California, witnessed the birth of two entire litters and with the aid of a stop watch even clocked the time required for each little mite to make the perilous journey and become safely sheltered in the pouch. The details of Reynolds' interesting observations await publication.

With the "mystery" of marsupial birth solved, we are prepared to pose another question which has frequently been raised in the literature: Once forcibly removed from the nipple, is the young opossum able to find it again and to receive it a second time into its mouth? Richard Owen had an opportunity more than a century ago of performing such an experiment on a kangaroo "in order to discover the nature of the connection between the mother and the pouch young, allegedly 'grown together', and to ascertain whether so small a foetus would manifest the powers of a voluntary agent in regaining the nipple." He detached a pouch young the day after its birth, which he had planned to witness but had missed because of miscalculating the gestation period. Two days after replacing

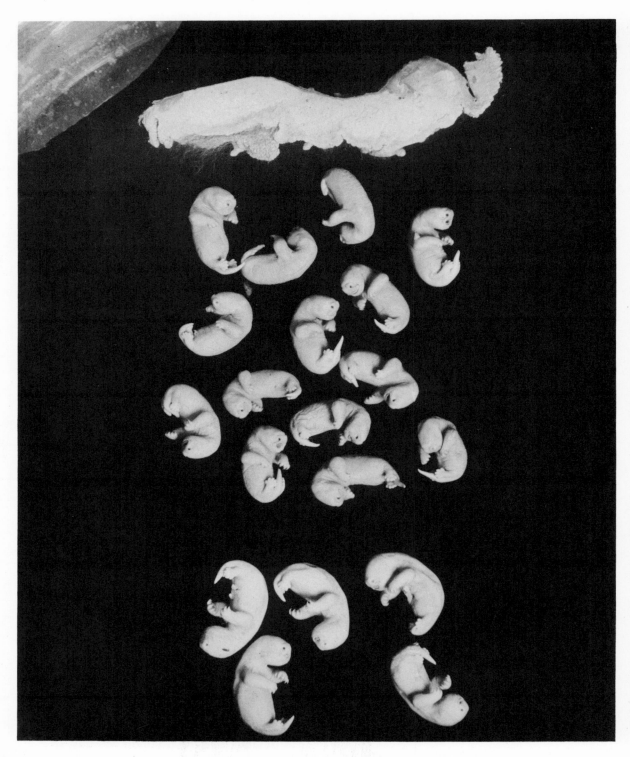

Fourteen newborn pouch young and five several days old. Above the embryos: slice of mammary glands with three small projecting nipples, which have been somewhat drawn out by one hour's sucking activity of the pouch young. Greatly enlarged.

96

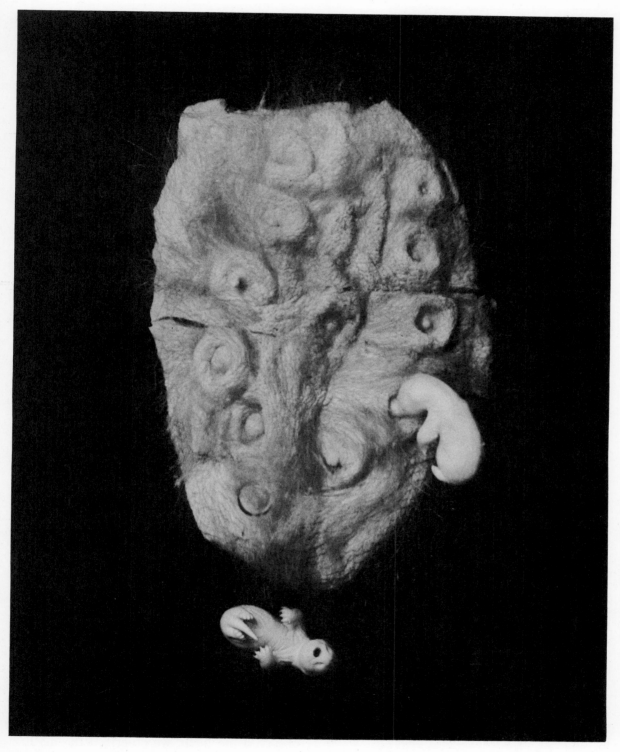

Skin from floor of pouch, showing arrangement of nipples (one not seen, because it has not been occupied). One of the ten-day-old young has been removed from its nipple; another is still attached. Greatly enlarged.

the detached young in the pouch, he found the nipple empty, the young lost. Later in a similar experiment he is said to have discovered the young reattached. Barton, as well as Geoffroy Saint-Hilaire, had previously proved that there is no organic fusion of the tissues of the nipple and those of the suckling mouth, so that, if done carefully, the pouch young can be removed without causing trauma and bleeding. This I have done hundreds of times to secure pouch young for study.

The question was fully considered by Waterhouse in his book *Marsupialia,* and he cited several experiments, the reports of which I have checked and found to be authentic.

In a letter addressed to the Secretary of the Zoological Society, and read before the scientific meeting on the 14th July 1840, Sir Robert Heron states that a young Kangaroo had by some accident got out of the pouch of its mother before the proper time, and some hours having elapsed before he could find his keeper, the little animal, which was quite naked, was scarcely alive when he arrived—the keeper however took it home, gave it milk, and by careful treatment, it quite recovered; it was then restored to the pouch, where it remained five days, at the time that a second letter from Sir R. Heron announced the fact to the society, and appeared perfectly well. [Presumably it was the young kangaroo that was quite well.]

Mr. Collie [Waterhouse's footnote: "On some particulars connected with the Natural History of the Kangaroos." Zoological Journal, vol. v. p. 239] describes the young of a species of Kangaroo . . . which he saw at Buache, or Garden Island, Western Australia, as being "nearly the size of the last and half the middle joint of one's little finger; its integuments of a flesh colour, and so transparent as to permit the higher coloured vessels and viscera to shine through them." This little foetus Mr. Collie detached from the nipple, and shortly afterwards he placed the extremity of the teat close to its mouth, and having held it there for a short time without perceiving any decided effort on the part of the young animal to regain its hold, he allowed the pouch to close. An hour afterwards the young was observed still unattached, but in two hours it had

hold of the teat, and was actively employed sucking.

Then in a footnote: "The mode by which the young Kangaroo reaches the pouch immediately after birth is not yet known."

A third observation cited by Waterhouse was made by Morgan, who removed a kangaroo young the size of a Norway rat "which after two hours' separation from the nipple, regained its hold, and sustained no injury from the interruption of the supply of nourishment."

Troughton mentions an interesting episode related to him by Farmer Joliff, who, while plowing, disturbed a marsupial mouse which had ten young clinging to her. When first noticed, she was slowly making her escape over the uneven clods. "On the young ones being removed the devoted creature remained near, and when the mites squeaked she answered the call by threading her way among the cluster until all were re-attached, when she sought cover under some bark."

In 1863, James G. Shute wrote a letter to the Boston Society of Natural History concerning an observation he had made on the birth of an opossum at Beaufort, South Carolina. After describing the manner of delivery (considerably at variance with our own), Shute proceeded as follows:

Immediately after the transfer of the young to the pouch, I removed one, by detaching it from the teat in order to ascertain if the movement of the foetus was instinctive. I found that it was at least partly voluntary, as it made an effort to regain its place in the pouch; and the same movement was made on the part of the parent to receive it, as at first. I did not notice any use of the lips or limbs of the parent during the transfer.

Our own experiments with pouch young an hour old were most convincing. Having observed the birth, we etherized the mother and tested the responses of the twenty-one young in the pouch. Of these, twelve were attached, though thirteen might have been,

98

as the Virginia opossum has that number of teats. The remaining nine, like all young of this species when born in excess of thirteen, were doomed to starvation. Our report reads:

With the mother anesthetized, we proceeded gently to pull off a number of embryos from the teats. The teats had already been drawn out from about a millimeter in height to double that length, doubtless by the traction of the embryos themselves. The bottom of the pouch certainly presented a busy scene with each member of the close-pressed litter engaged in very active breathing and sucking movements.

One detached young, placed near the vulva, crawled readily back into the pouch. Two or three others gained the teats after some delay, and one wanderer, which lost out in the first scramble, found a vacated teat and attached itself even after twenty minutes' delay. Whenever we tilted the skin, the embryos invariably traveled upward, even away from the pouch.

Because of this last-named tendency the young were listed as "negatively geotropic," on which unfortunate expression I shall philosophize below.

Dr. McCrady performed this experiment many times. He wrote:

At my first success I had called in two witnesses. Thirteen days and two hours after an observed copulation a young opossum had been found in the pouch (its actual birth not having been observed). I removed the fetus from the nipple and placed it on its mother's abdomen. The hair was dry and the fetus stuck to it so that although he struggled vigorously he was unable to make progress in any direction. Wetting my finger I moistened the skin of the fetus. The latter's movements quickly became effective. In less than three minutes it had clambered up this inclined plane of its mother's abdomen and disappeared into the pouch. Three minutes later I opened the pouch and found it safely attached to another nipple—not the one it had first appropriated.

The significance of this experiment seems to be that though the mother does not pick up the young, her licking the hair of the abdomen seems to be an essential one.

In a similar experiment Audubon and Bach-man went a step further by interchanging young between two parents. These experiments would seem to have clinched the matter a century ago, in a rather spectacular manner. They report:

We tried another experiment that suggested itself to us. Believing that the mother would not readily adopt the young of another, or afford them any assistance, we removed six of the ten that composed her brood, returned two of her own to the pouch, together with three others fully double the size, that had been obtained from another female. She was soon observed doubled up with her nose in the pouch, and continued so for an hour, when she was examined and one of her own ones was found attached to the teat. Seven hours afterwards she was examined again, and both the small ones were attached, but the three larger ones still remained sprawling about the pouch. On the following morning, it was ascertained that the mother had adopted the strangers as the whole family of different sizes were deriving sustenance from her.

As in all science, so in that infinitesimal branch thereof, "possumology," the solution of one problem raises others. Among the most perplexing questions that have been raised by physiologists are these: By what senses is the newborn young guided in its journey to the only haven where survival is possible? And what is the cue that makes it stop its search and attach itself once it makes contact with the tiny nipple? In Barton's day, and indeed much closer to the present time, such a problem would be dismissed by declaring that the acts are "instinctive." Today "instinct" has come to connote an area of ignorance of factors that operate to arouse and direct an animal's activities. We no longer say, "Such and such an act is purely instinctive, and attempts to explain it are therefore futile." Instead, we try to discover the factors that condition the act.

The word *instinct* has trapped many a naturalist into mental lethargy. So have high-sounding expressions that on analysis are misleading or meaningless. I confess to having been led into such a trap myself, by the very pouch young that we are studying. Upon noticing that the tiny opossums always crawled upward on the inclined abdomen of the mother, I stated categorically that the newborn opossum was "negatively geotropic," i.e., tending to move away from the earth's surface, just as a housefly tends to move upwards on a window screen. In the same way roots of plants are geotropic, since they always grow downwards, and stems are negatively geotropic, since they grow upwards. That phrase "negatively geotropic" sounded good when applied to the newborn opossum, and the idea agreed with part, but only a part, of what we saw.

Questioning this interpretation, McCrady was led into an involved series of researches. He and his group of experts were studying the development of the ear in the growing pouch young when, lo! they discovered that at the time of birth the opossum possesses no functional inner ear at all—no hearing organ, the cochlea, and no balancing organ, the semicircular canals. It follows from this that the expression "negative geotropism" cannot possibly apply to the newborn opossum, for there is no organ provided to record the pull of gravity. That this function does not begin until the forty-first day of marsupial life was determined by Longworthy.

What, then, is the reason that the opossum young travels up? The real explanation, demonstrated by McCrady and his colleagues, was simple and quite in line with common sense and careful observation.

Everyone is acquainted with the old-fashioned gate latch which, by virtue of its eccentric pivot, swings like a pendulum and when at rest keeps the gate closed. The upward traveling opossum pouch young is like that—it is pivoted at the front end of the body, namely, by the front legs. These are provided with strong claws and are the sole organs of locomotion, while the hind limbs, being mere undeveloped five-lobed pads, are dragged along passively. The clambering opossum in moving forward must of necessity move upward. So when an opossum mother sits up, as she does while giving birth, the young cannot help traveling to the pouch, because this is up.

The same mechanical explanation holds also for the kangaroo. It is especially interesting to note that the hind legs, which in the adult are enormous compared with the front, are undeveloped in the fetal kangaroo as in the opossum. The newborn kangaroo is propelled into the pouch by the front legs; later, its hind legs develop tremendously and in the adult are the animal's only organs of locomotion.

The upward directing mechanism described assures the safety of the young marsupial born with so primitive a brain that it can hardly be said to have a will of its own. Richard Owen and others speak of its "voluntary" acts. If the opossum pouch embryo has a "will," conscious will does not reside in that part of the brain where we think it does, for the newborn possesses no such part. It is certain, therefore, that the acts of the newborn marsupial are all reflex, that is, are mediated entirely by the spinal cord and lower brain centers, for the simple reason that it has no other.

Although careful observation and persistent investigational work have cleared up the mystery of marsupial birth, some modern accounts still are tinged with legend. As late as 1936 the *Encyclopedia Americana* was a hundred years behind the times as regards the newborn's trip to the pouch. In 1940 a writer in the Works Progress Administration's *American Wild Life* had the young guided by a streak of milk, and he says that they remain dormant for fifty-five days. But Chalane in his *Mammals of North America,* Hamilton in his *American Mammals,* Storer in his *General Zoology,* and many others have described the birth of the opossum correctly.

My own sleuthing activities were reported

by an opossum fan in the following manner in an editorial of the *Bertram* (Texas) *Enterprise* of July 13, 1920:

Now that Carl has spied on Mother Opossum in the hour of her delivery and discussed her negligence about getting her little ones into their nursery, what is he going to do about it? Wherein is the discovery important to science and to bread-and-butter making? We know two things, as a result of Carl's vigils, which will occasion all lovers of 'Possum and 'Taters much alarm. First, that since the tiny creatures must find their way into the marsupium unaided, the opossum industry is in constant peril. Second, since the 'possum newborn weighs only ¾ of a grain our respect for a five-pound 'possum increases; he is equivalent in weight to 46,666 2/3 embryo 'possums. We noticed Carl's advertisement for 'possums some time ago, but thought he wanted them to eat. He fed upon them in the mountain section of Travis County while he was County School Superintendent years ago, and out of sheer gratitude to their humble contributions to his diet of poorer days, he now uses the equipment of the great University of Texas in spying out their last secret.

14

Birth of the Kangaroo

From the damp forests of tropical Queensland to the sun-bathed centre, across to the Leeuwin where the sun sets west of Australia, the mysteries of marsupial birth and transference of the young to the pouch have provided keen bush naturalists with endless food for argument." Thus wrote Ellis Troughton in his *Furred Animals of Australia.*

It is not surprising that Australians from time to time published notices that they had seen the newborn kangaroo fetus crawl by its own efforts into the mother's pouch. Since these reports appeared in obscure newspapers, sometimes in the form of "Letters to the Editor," and since they were written by amateurs, they were long overlooked by naturalists, even those living in Australia. What may have contributed materially to their neglect was the fact that these observations were at striking variance with the accepted notions, held to be "authoritative" because printed in books. After the publication of our own report on the birth of the opossum, the old observations of the amateurs were suddenly considered significant.

As early as 1830, Collie quoted an officer of H.M.S. *Success,* who observed a kangaroo in the act of parturition. When the young one was expelled, the officer told Collie, the

mother was resting against the cage, partly on her side, partly on her back, the hind legs apart. The young crept through the fur toward the pouch, progressing "as expeditiously as a snail." Collie's informant, unaware of the significance of his observations, had removed the young without letting it complete the journey.

A completed journey made by a newborn kangaroo was described by the Hon. L. Hope in the *Transactions* of the Philosophical Society of Queensland. "My observations have reference only to the mode of transference of the embryo to the pouch, which I now believe to be effected by the embryo itself; or, at any rate, with very little assistance from the mother, and that almost unconsciously given. I heard lately of an instance of the same appearances having been observed by a kangaroo hunter, and was pleased to find the confirmation of his story by my own experience."

A more detailed description is that of a certain Mr. A. Goerling, whose article appeared in the Perth *Western Mail* of January 3, 1913. This was quoted in my 1920 paper on the birth of the opossum:

The question of how the young kangaroo comes into the pouch has long been looked upon as answered. According to observations made, the young is born and placed on the pap by its mother, and this view has been accepted by zoologists.

On the 25th of February, 1906, I had the good fortune to make a most interesting and astounding observation. . . . On the morning of the above mentioned date I was attracted by the peculiar behavior of a female *Macropus rufus*. She refused the feed placed before her; and on seeing blood marks in the cage, I came to the conclusion that the animal had just given birth to a young one. She was sitting in that resting position in which kangaroos can often be seen, the tail passed forward through the legs. Thus she was sitting almost entirely on the thick part of the tail. She took no notice of my presence, although not more than three weeks in captivity, and was busy licking and cleaning herself. Presently she lifted her head, when I was astonished to see a young kangaroo clinging to the long fur about four inches below the opening of the pouch.

It moved about slowly, very slowly, through the fur upwards, using the arms in its progress, and continually moving its head from side to side, thus assisting the upward movement. Nearly 30 minutes were required by the little wanderer to reach the top of the pouch. During the whole of this time the mother paid no attention to her offspring, offering no assistance, and leaving it entirely to its own exertions. She then became restless; and not wishing to disturb her, I moved a short distance away, when she at once started to feed. A little later I paid another visit to the cage. She was sitting upright, the young one had disappeared, but the fur was still bearing evidence of the struggle, a plain visible track to and ending at the top of the pouch. . . .

My observation proves that the newborn Kangaroo has to look after its own safety and reach the pouch without the mother's assistance.

Goerling's conclusions were fully corroborated by J. S. Munro, a keeper in the Taronga Park in Sydney. As reported in Troughton's book, Munro and his witnesses saw their animal vigorously licking the fur between the base of the tail and the pouch, making a smooth track, as it were, for the fetus to travel on. The emphasis in their report was rightly placed on the independent action of the newborn in its travel to the pouch, for the observers were fully cognizant of the fact that they had a stubborn traditional belief to combat. Later, Noel Bennet, founder of Kaola Park, a refuge for the Australian Teddy bear, mentioned seeing a kaola embryo making its unaided journey to the pouch.

More complete observations have since been made in American and European zoological parks. One report comes from the Leipzig Zoo. The gist of Ernst Pinkert's observations follows: On March 2, 1888, on an inspection tour of the park, Pinkert saw a kangaroo of the species *M. rufus* lying on the ground shivering as if she had a chill. She avoided other animals. After a half-hour the kangaroo sat up and manipulated her pouch with her forepaws and inserted her head, licking and cleaning. She grasped the lower abdomen and pressed the pendant part. She fought off her yearling young one. After two hours of manipulations the female sat firmly

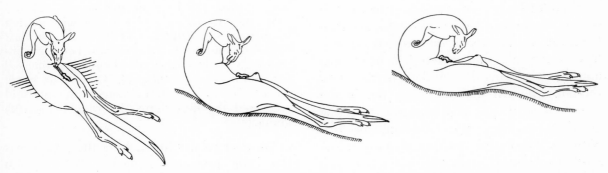

Kangaroo female licking a pathway on which the newborn young may travel to the pouch. Sketches by F. Schmidt-Hoendorf.

103

in a corner, back to wall, tail between legs, which were stretched out and spread apart. She was thus sitting on her sacrum, a posture which made her genital opening more visible.

She now supported herself on her forefeet and bent over so that her mouth was at the vulva, while her front legs were pulled back out of the way. She then cleansed the vulva by licking, and when she had raised herself somewhat, an object about the size of a finger-stall appeared, flesh colored, flecked with drops of blood. She then bent over again so far that one could not now see what she was doing. But when she arose once more, the observer could see that she was inserting an object into the pouch with her mouth, while she held open her pouch with her forepaws. In conclusion the author affirms that the mother's hands were not used in the transfer, as they are too awkward, and anyway were occupied with keeping the pouch open. With the mouth, so Pinkert concluded, the female placed the young into the pouch.

For decades this description has been quoted repeatedly. It seems a straightforward story and would be acceptable, with only slight reservations, except for the overwhelming evidence of others. I rather believe that Pinkert missed the crucial moment of the transfer, since he mentioned difficulty in seeing what the mother was doing.

Another fortunate occasion similar to that experienced by Pinkert was offered in the zoo at Halle, Germany, in 1933, as related by F. Schmidt-Hoendorf. According to this observer, the female kangaroo sat back on her haunches so that the abdomen was more or less horizontal. She moved her head back and forth, licking the abdomen. At about three-quarters of an inch from the genital orifice, a small naked young one was seen crawling peculiarly, searching back and forth with its head and moving upward on its mother's belly. The female had apparently licked a track on which the fetus advanced. The mother paid no attention to the young.

It required five minutes for the embryo to reach the edge of the pouch, whereupon it bored into the fold and disappeared.

The author had on a former occasion observed a similar wet track on the hair of a female and had noticed a small amount of blood on the floor beside her. The movements of the young are described as seal-like or caterpillar-like. Schmidt-Hoendorf expressed the opinion that the track, smoothed down with saliva, directs the young, which is unpleasantly pricked by the dry hair when it deviates from its proper course. This article the author illustrated with an instructive sketch.

Such a path of matted hair, wet by the mother's tongue, was seen by L. Harrison Matthews in the Clifton Zoological Gardens of Bristol.

Corroborative testimony comes from two American zoological parks. On March 30, 1921, George F. Morse, Jr., had the following experience in the Franklin Park Zoo, Boston. His account, written out for me from memory, his notes having been destroyed by fire, agrees well with the version quoted by Troughton in his book.

The female placed her tail extending forward between her legs. There was no evidence that the animal suffered labor pains. The youngster was born on the base of the tail and at once started to squirm and wriggle up through the abdominal hair towards the entrance of the pouch. The day was cold and raw and the animal house unheated. In 25 minutes the youngster had reached the level of the pouch, but unfortunately to one side. It was evidently getting weak from the struggle and the cold. The last five or six minutes the mother was becoming increasingly restless; scratching herself she knocked it off on the floor of the cage. The mother made no attempt to find it. I entered the cage and recovered the dead fetus. Its weight was 19½ grains.

More successful in reaching the pouch was the little Bennett's kangaroo baby which keeper Riley of the Bronx Zoo saw born. In this case, also, the mother sat on the floor of

104

the cage. On the flat table of the base of the tail the young was born in the usual fashion. Within a minute or so after it appeared, it began to scramble about "as if looking for something," and the next instant it rather nimbly scrambled up the hair covering the abdomen of the mother, found the pouch, and quickly entered it.

In view of the evidence presented in this chapter and the preceding one, we may well agree with Professor Matthews when he says, "The neonatal marsupial crawls into the marsupium by its own efforts and is not transferred by the mother." Troughton sums up the matter thus: "Expressing it simply and conclusively, it may be said that newly born marsupials seek the teat within the sheltering pouch with a flash of instinctive energy which lapses after the goal is reached. To suppose that they are born upon the teats . . . is about as reasonable as expecting a calf to be born on the teat of a cow." Mostly correct; only the presumption that this peculiar instinctive

behavior, the ability to find the nipple, "lapses after the goal is reached" is not in keeping with my own evidence. As already explained, the ability does not lapse suddenly. The behavioral pattern seems to be somewhat different from that of newborn monkeys and human babies, who are able to support their chubby weight immediately they are born— an acrobatic feat that is lost after a few days.

It would seem hardly to be expected that future observations will make necessary any revision of the conclusion here recorded, namely, that the kangaroo as well as the opossum newborn reaches and finds and grasps the nipple without more than accessory assistance from the mother, such as licking the young free of its envelopes and perhaps licking a streak of matted hair from vulva to pouch. Eyewitnesses aplenty have vouched for the independent trek of the newborn marsupial to its haven, the mother's warm pouch.

15

The Brood Pouch in Nature

IT WAS AN OPOSSUM with a well-developed pouch, probably a member of the species *Didelphis marsupialis,* which Pinzón captured in Brazil four and a half centuries ago. This and similar species, all with well-developed pouches, were encountered by the Spaniards in Mexico. In North America the English and French found *Didelphis virginiana,* which is the only opossum occurring north of the thirtieth parallel of latitude. Since the range of this species reaches northward into the land of snow and ice and since the young are born in late February, March, or early April, according to the latitude, its young have especial need for a warm, moist cradle.

The margin of the pouch is provided with a well-developed sphincter muscle, the contraction of which closes the opening as one closes an old-fashioned, pre-zipper tobacco sac with a drawstring, not "like a door which can be opened or closed when wanted," as Father Sanchez Labrado wrote in 1770. This sphincter is so efficient in Chironectes, or yapok, the water opossum, that the young are fully protected when the mother takes to the water. The Virginia opossum, also known as a good swimmer, can likewise convert her pouch into a watertight compartment.

On the actual temperature of the inside of the pouch when occupied I have no data. It is presumably higher than that of the unoccupied pouch by virtue of the rich blood supply of the actively secreting mammary glands.

The body temperature of the adult opossum is peculiarly low as compared with that of other mammals of corresponding size. The German anatomist and artist Selenka, who in 1887 imported a hundred Virginia opossums for his laboratory at the University of Würzburg, reported the temperature to be about 97° F. George Wislocki, anatomist and naturalist, took the temperature of a number of tropical opossums as well as the Virginian and found it to range between 95° and 97°. The low body temperature is, therefore, normal for the opossum, in the tropics as well as in the northern winter. That the animal can maintain its body temperature in a cold environment has been demonstrated experimentally by G. E. Johnston. When his subjects were placed for some hours in a refrigerator at 40° F., their body temperature dropped only three to six degrees.

With a body temperature around 97° the three- to six-pound opossum fails to fit into the chart of size-temperature relationships of the animal series from the finger-sized shrew to the elephant. There is no explanation for this instance of nonconformity.

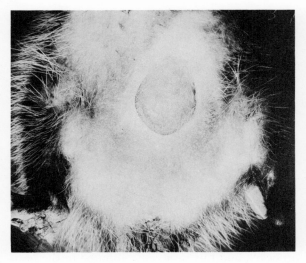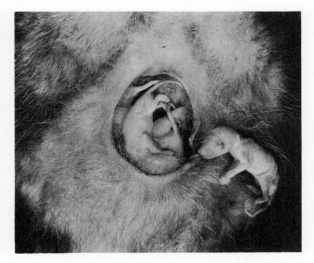

Left: opossum pouch, unoccupied. Right: occupied. The greatly lengthened nipple serves not only as milk duct but also as tether, giving considerable freedom of movement to the crowded family.

An analysis of the air which the pouch young have to breathe is interesting. Almeida and Rocha reported that this air ranges from 2 per cent to nearly 5 per cent of carbon dioxide and 15 to 19 per cent of oxygen, as against 0.25 per cent of carbon dioxide and 21 per cent of oxygen for outside air. In other words, the pouch young breathe and re-breathe air that has eight to twenty times the normal content of carbon dioxide. This is shown in the six analyses recorded in the chart.

	1	2	3	4	5	6
Percentage of carbon dioxide	2.77	4.80	1.87	3.20	2.97	4.50
Percentage of oxygen	16.01	17.30	19.31	17.10	18.02	15.04

This accumulation of carbon dioxide, a waste product, in the living quarters of an animal is as surprising as it is unique, for we are accustomed to think of such an environment as harmful. However, since Nature always knows best, it is the scientist's business to try to discover how the excess carbon dioxide might be beneficial to the embryonic pouch young. It is interesting to speculate on possible reasons. Carbon dioxide is known to constitute the indispensable stimulus to the activity of the breathing center in the medulla; in short, carbon dioxide keeps us breathing. The oxygen furnished the patient in an oxygen tent contains an admixture of 5 per cent carbon dioxide. So for the present we may conclude that the high percentage of carbon dioxide in the opossum pouch must in some way play a useful role. It has, however, been possible to raise in ordinary room air a young opossum detached from the pouch. Perhaps the high carbon dioxide content of the pouch is just Nature's margin of safety. But the matter needs study, as some fundamental physiology is involved. We do know that all embryos—and marsupial young are virtual embryos—utilize sugar and carry on internal respiration quite differently from more mature individuals.

Another question that was posed by early writers is this one: Does the male possess a pouch? A foolish question, perhaps; yet Rochefort in 1665 had endowed the male with a pouch and suggested that he participated in the nourishment of the young. How did it come about that such a purely female attribute was transferred to the male? The idea was still toyed with a half-century later when the anatomist William Cowper, discoverer of the gland named after him, observed in the course of his dissections that the male opossum also possessed marsupial bones. Since these were supposed to serve as support for the pouch, why should the male possess such bones unless he had a pouch? Dr. Cowper examined the appropriate region of his specimen, pushed in the skin, but could not make the pocket resemble a pouch—the skin easily turned out again upon his withdrawing his fingers. He wrote: "Whether, therefore, 'tis capable of being formed into a Pouch or Marsupium upon Occasion, I shall pose as a Query to be resolved by those that live where they breed: 'Whether they ever observe the Male to receive the Young ones, as do the Females.' "

Very conservatively stated. The question has, of course, been answered in the negative; but Dr. Cowper did very well with the one male carcass that he had, as did Dr. Tyson with one female. Had these experimenters been "living where opossums breed," they would certainly have discovered the simple, logical truth: that only the female opossum is equipped with a nursery. It is a fact, though, that in the infant pouch young the males do possess the rudiments of mammary glands, variable in number. The female starts and ends with thirteen, plus or minus one or two, while the male has fewer, and these are more irregularly placed. In a four-grain young the future marsupium is already clearly indicated, and on this basis at this early stage the sexes can be differentiated with fair certainty.

The brood pouch was, however, not created for the opossum alone; it is not even the exclusive property of the Marsupialia. The device for the protection and nutrition of the young is found throughout the animal kingdom, from mollusks and crustaceans up to fishes and amphibians; and without much stretch of the imagination one may include two species of birds, namely, two kinds of penguins.

We may cite first certain bats that give birth while hanging upside down, their usual posture when asleep. H. B. Sherman has many times witnessed the birth of the Florida bat *Myotis austroriparius* and has furnished (*Journal of Mammalogy*, 1930) a vivid picture of this most unusual mode of parturition.

Twins is the rule. The parturient mother usually hangs head down, let us say from the side of a vertically placed rough board, catching hold by her feet and "thumbs," i.e. the claws placed at the angle of the wing. In this position, with the tail describing an arc, the membrane running between the femora and including the tail makes a pocket, and this cavity is continued to the base of the wing. The arrangement forms a safety net to catch the young when born. The illustration shows a pair of twins safely held in the cavities of the relaxed wing folds, from which they soon make successful efforts to find the breasts, one on each side. Once attached to the nipple, the young hold on to the fur with their claws and are even carried around in dizzy flight in which the mother captures aerial insects to feed herself and her two husky young.

Whether one is justified in attributing a brood pouch to the emperor or king penguin is a matter of definition. The facts are these, according to E. A. Wilson, naturalist of Captain Robert F. Scott's voyage in the *Discovery* during 1901-1904. The emperor penguin of Antarctica lays its single egg in the coldest month of the year, when the temperature averages 18° F. below zero and often falls as low as 68°. Female and male share in the incubation of the egg and the care of the young, which is placed on the dorsum of the parent's feet, wedged in between the legs and the abdomen. Over the egg and later the hatched chick, there is a protective flap of heavily feathered skin. "When the chick is hungry or inquisitive," Wilson tells us, "it pokes out from under the maternal (or paternal) lappet a piebald head of black and white, emitting its shrill and persistent pipe until the mother (or the father) fills it up."

Frogs offer a number of striking examples

Pouchless marmosa nursing (and defending) three young attached to her nipples. Photograph by Marjorie Shanafelt.

of the adaptation of certain organs as brood pouches. Perhaps the most bizarre case is that of Darwin's frog (*Rhinoderma darwinii*), the species first seen by Charles Darwin when H. M. S. *Beagle* stopped in Chile on its round-the-world scientific expedition. In this species it is the male that carries the tadpoles in his gular pouch or resonating chamber. First he calls his mate to his side and sings to her. When her eggs are mature, the male spouse is rewarded for his song by having a batch of eggs stuffed down his throat, after which silence reigns in the household: the voice box has become the brood chamber. In the wall of the pouch there is a rich network of blood vessels from which the tadpoles, some twenty of them, receive their supply of oxygen.

Other frogs, the Surinam toad, for example, incubate their tadpoles in pockets in the skin of the back. In such cases the protection afforded favors survival; a dozen or two young a season are sufficient to insure the preservation of the race, whereas our common frogs must produce hundreds and even thousands of eggs to make up for the losses sustained by the delicate tadpoles in the presence of predatory enemies lurking behind every plant and pebble of their environment.

Among fishes, too, the male may participate in the care of the eggs and small fry. The most unusual case is that of the sea horse, familiar to all visitors of marine aquaria. When a pair mates, while the male expels the sperm into the sea water between them to insure fertilization of the eggs, the female places these into the abdominal pouch of her mate. Here the relation of the young to the pouch wall is the same as in Darwin's frog, in that the highly vascular lining of the pouch furnishes oxygen for the young until time for them to leave the paternal shelter and to hide among the water plants. In both the sea horse and Darwin's frog it is the male and not the female that becomes pregnant.

Crustacea, too, are replete with examples of the care of eggs and young in well-defined brood pouches of the parent. The crayfish carries hundreds of eggs attached to its abdominal appendages. The common water flea of our ponds and rain barrels possesses a closed brood pouch harboring eight to ten eggs. One crustacean, the shrimp Mysis, has, for obvious reasons, received the popular name "opossum shrimp."

While countless forms other than marsupials possess the brood pouch, in many true marsupials, paradoxically, the pouch is either rudimentary or lacking altogether. One example is that of the mouse opossum, Marmosa, best known in this country as a banana-boat stowaway. Australia holds dozens of species of marsupials which are pouchless or nearly so—true marsupials, of course, by every other criterion.

The manner in which the offspring of pouchless marsupials are carried about as they cling to the mother's nipples differs in no respect from the way in which young field mice and wood rats are transported. The Aus-

109

tralian rodent *Leporillus jonesi*, the stick-nest rat, was once taken for a pouchless marsupial because of its habit of carrying young suspended from its nipples, which are grasped firmly in the youngsters' mouths. The young are dragged along on their backs, even when the mother runs rapidly over rough terrain. W. B. Richardson, who studied the American wood rat's growth and development, describes the relation of mother and babies: "When attached to the nipple, the young remain relaxed with little regard for their position. Thus attached, the female transports the relaxed young wherever necessary, the young dragging along without regard for equilibrium. When the female is excited, I have seen her run about the partially destroyed nest with the young dangling behind, bobbing over the debris."

Gander's descriptions agree with Richardson's and in addition he has the following story to tell of a baby wood rat finding a foster parent:

A student at the Institute, Leroy Arnold, relates an interesting incident. He had trapped an adult female under a house at Monte Robles and kept her alive in captivity. During the following day a loud squeaking was heard in an old bird's nest high in the branches of a large liveoak. The captive was much aroused by this and uttered a squeal in answer. Arnold climbed to the nest and found there a single baby bushrat with its eyes not yet open. He carried it down and placed it

Wood rat mother dragging her two large sucklings attached to her teats. Photograph by W. B. Richardson.

110

with the female he had trapped and it attached itself to one of the teats. She seemed pleased to have the little one with her again.

A number of observers have marveled at the colossal burdens some mothers carry. Woods-Jones, for example, describes a case: "Krefft's Pouched Mouse has seven young. There is practically no pouch. The young cling to the nipples for over a month and she staggers around with this considerable burden." The same holds for the crest-tailed marsupial mouse, according to Troughton: "The pouch is practically absent, but the small young are protected by a shallow ridge; they cling to the teats for over a month. The mother is a curious sight staggering about in search of insects or in attacking a mouse, with about seven large young clinging to her teats."

The opossum and rodent races have survived for millions of years with or without the pouch and may be expected to continue to do so indefinitely. While a writer in *The Naturalist's Library* "cannot help regarding the absence of the pouch in some Marsupialia an indication of an approach in these animals to a higher order," the question whether in these animals the pouch is going out or coming in, geologically speaking, is an academic one. The marsupial animal has more truly fundamental characters for the evolutionists to rationalize about. The pouch has served to impress mankind and to stimulate certain persons to write books about it.

16

The Pouch Young

PROBABLY INFLUENCED by the legend of the bear cub born a shapeless mass of flesh which the mother has to lick into form, early naturalists described the newborn opossum in somewhat similar terms. Palpable misapprehensions about pouch young were prevalent in the best zoology textbooks of their day. The Frenchman Milne-Edwards, who merits just fame for being one of the first to stress the physiological approach to the study of zoology, wrote in his *Eléments de zoologie* that the young are not developed as ordinarily in the uterus, but are prematurely expelled and are born as tiny gelatinous bodies, shapeless and incapable of movement, with no organs distinctly formed.

Another pioneer in the study of reproductive processes, the Frenchman Pouchet, in his *Zoologie classique,* described the newborn opossum as "only a simple ovule, still bathed in albuminous fluid, which finds a place on the teat." But even as late as 1924, in *The Book of Popular Science,* an author still speaks of the "motionless little fragments of life which the marsupial mother pops into the pouch." These samples reveal a lack of acquaintance with the material which authors make bold to handle; they take their cues from the older literature, and items are often

dressed up to give natural history a sensational flavor—all of which serves to conceal the true picture.

Already in 1834, Richard Owen had described the activities of the kangaroo newborn quite objectively:

Twelve hours after birth it resembled an earthworm in colour and semi-transparency of the integument; adhered firmly to the nipple, breathed strongly but slowly and moved its forelegs when disturbed. Its body was bent upon its abdomen, its short tail tucked between its legs, which were one-third shorter than the forelegs, but with the three divisions of the toes now distinct. It measured one and one-sixth inches.

Around the middle of the last century several naturalists made careful scientific observations on the opossum pouch young, reporting their findings accurately and unsensationally and yet with an enthusiasm that was contagious.

Dr. Charles D. Meigs was one of these careful investigators, as already pointed out. Having acquired a mother opossum with recently born young, he studied them with as diligent care as his medical practice permitted. From time to time he removed individual young for minute examination. His descriptions belied the erroneous statements

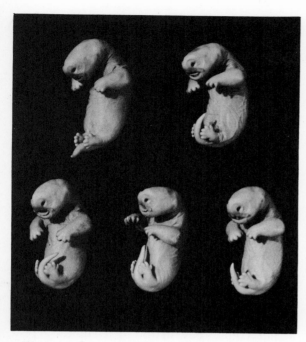

Five newborn pouch young from a litter observed in parturition.

baby opossum's being warm-blooded—that is not a matter of philosophy but of physiology; and physiology tells us that the young opossum is not able to control its body temperature. The reason for this is that the part of the brain that regulates temperature is not yet functional; it is indeed not yet functional in the newborn human baby. The opossum pouch young is kept warm solely by the mother's body heat.

Different species of animals are born at very different states of development. After a twenty-one-day gestation the rat and the mouse are blind, helpless creatures. By way of contrast, the guinea pig at sixty-three days of gestation is ready to supplement its mother's milk with solid food; and a newborn elephant, calf, or colt is almost immediately able to trudge some miles beside its dam. The most helpless creature at birth, the opossum, has just enough equipment for its short but precarious journey to the pouch. For this its front legs are well developed and its fingers armed with sharp claws, which are deciduous, dropping off some time after the baby is safely ensconced in the pouch. At birth the hind limbs are retarded in development and useless, which holds also for the kangaroo.

A useful and precocious organ of the pouch young is the tongue, with which the animal enclasps the nipple and holds on for dear life. Associated with the tongue is a strong set of facial muscles. As the photographs show, the young possesses a muzzle reminiscent of the "sucker" of the frog tadpole.

Sucking begins the moment contact is made with the nipple. Within an hour, as a result of the traction exerted by the young, the length of the nipple is doubled. Gradually the nipple becomes longer and longer and more slender, serving finally not only as a tube for the transport of milk but also as a tether to give freedom of movement to the growing occupants—up to thirteen—in the crowded pouch. A terminal swelling may

of the past. Already at the time of birth, he tells us with a certain admiration for the vitality of the fetus, it was not a mere gob of shapeless albuminous matter, but "a chylopoietic [i.e., digesting], warm blooded, oxygenating, innervating, free willing life." He goes on to affirm that "all the means of carrying on an independent life are as fully enjoyed by the marsupial fetus, as by the young of an elephant at the teat, or a Balaena whale whose young is said to measure twenty-seven feet in length. If that be so," he adds, "all mystery as to marsupial life is at an end—save that of adaptation to the nipple." This last remnant of mystery, he mournfully predicts, will never be solved. Dr. Meigs, however, did exaggerate a bit the degree of development attained by the newborn, as will be explained below.

Whether the opossum is a "free willing" organism depends on one's viewpoint; evidently Meigs was not a mechanist. Philosophy does not seem to have worried him, and the battles between the mechanists and the vitalists had not yet opened up. But as to the develop on the teat and probably helps to anchor the young. With the nipple uninterruptedly in the mouth and the powerful tongue pressing it against the middle of the upper gum, what will be the effect of the pressure on the development of the teeth, specifically the upper incisors? Need the mother opossum worry that her little ones will eventually require the services of an orthodontist to straighten the front teeth? Not at all. In her wisdom Dame Nature has solved this problem for the opossum in the simplest fashion possible, dispensing with the front milk teeth altogether; the milk teeth come in only on the sides. Some marsupial species, however, do have rudiments of the front milk teeth, mere vestiges, like the bony splints that in the modern horse represent the second and fourth digits of his three-toed ancestors.

The precocity of the marsupial newborn that has elicited wonderment appertains, however, only to certain structures other than the brain. His is the most primitive brain among newborn mammals. Its outstanding feature is the total lack of cortical structures, of which there is not even a rudiment or beginning. All of the functions over which Dr. Meigs justly exclaimed are carried out by the medulla, most primitive part of the brain, and by the spinal cord.

During the fifty or sixty days of development in the pouch the young grows not only in size but also in the maturation of its organs. The maturation of the nerves, muscles, and sense organs manifests itself in the animal's reactions, which have been minutely recorded by neurologist Langworthy. By means of painstaking experiments he was able to correlate the structural development with behavioral changes and reactions. His study resulted in the basic and significant discovery that nerves are able to carry impulses before they are provided with fatty sheaths, the "insulating" layer around the nerve fibers. A synopsis of the behavioral changes, as recorded by Langworthy, is presented below.

At seven days of age the little opossums could climb a rough surface such as a piece of gauze by making alternate beats of the forelegs, in the same manner as we first described the action of the newborn. The tail at seven days wrapped itself around a pencil, which argues for a precocious appearance of the prehensile function of this extremity. These reflexes, as well as the sucking and the side-to-side movements, evidently designed to find the nipple, were also present after the greater part of the brain had been removed, leaving only the medulla for the control of breathing.

At thirty-six days the same activities were still manifested; with the forelegs the young could grasp a cord but could not yet climb it, nor could they maintain a standing posture. These findings correlate well with the reports, mentioned elsewhere, that the pouch young removed from their teats can find and recover them again.

At forty-one days the young had the ability to right themselves, to balance themselves, and to walk a few steps before falling over, which indicated that the balancing mechanism, located in the semicircular canals of the inner ear, was beginning to function. At this time the young, when disturbed, began to make high-pitched cries (Lorenz Oken spoke of these as "sneezing" sounds).

At forty-six days the righting reflex was not much better developed, and while the young were able to hang on a rope, they made no efforts to climb. In correlation with the improved muscular control, the nerves, on microscopic examination, showed considerable maturation.

At fifty days McCrady found that the young began to react to sound and that by the seventy-seventh day they had arrived at an essentially adult condition with regard to hearing. Thereafter sensitivity to the higher tones developed gradually.

At fifty-four days (length of body 77 mm.),

according to Langworthy, hind legs were still shorter than the front. The young opossums assumed a standing position spontaneously and crawled rather pertly, however still using only the precocious front legs. The young could now support their weight by the tail. The fur was considerably developed; the eyes still closed.

At fifty-six days the pouch young were able to climb a cord. This growing independence indicated that they would soon be ready to detach themselves from the nipple.

At sixty-two days the young, now the size of mice, had their eyes open, their mouths gaping, and they could leave the nipple and regain it at will. They could walk well, but the front legs were under better control than the still smaller hind legs. Even the litter mates from which the cerebrum had been removed could hang by the tail.

At sixty-four days the hind legs had caught up with the front ones in size and were under equally good control.

At sixty-seven days the young, now the size of young rats and well furred, were able to run fast and climb with great agility. Their nervous and muscular systems were now quite "mature." The young were ready to be carried about by clinging to the hair and fur of the mother.

This study illustrates the part that physical development plays in any animal's ability to perform. The work of Dr. Gesell of Yale applies the same principle to children and warns us not to expect the impossible of them at too early a stage of maturation.

In spite of the accessibility of marsupial pouch young for careful study, superficial and faulty observation has led to a number of specific misconceptions concerning the relation of the pouch young to the mother. Marston Bates is right when he says, in *The Nature of Natural History* (1950): "The slowness with which descriptive science has developed makes it plain that the process is not as simple as it seems."

To begin with, authors have underestimated the capabilities of the pouch young by presuming that they are too weak to draw their mother's milk and that, as a consequence, the mother must needs pump the milk through the nipples into the mouths of the babies. Geoffroy Saint-Hilaire in 1826 considered this problem with reference to the kangaroo and came to these conclusions: the young kangaroo does not possess the necessary apparatus for sucking; and the muscles of the mother's abdomen are adapted to pumping the milk. Taking the matter quite seriously, Richard Owen even identified the muscle that does the work. The marsupial bones, which extend upwards from the pelvic bone along the pouch, he explained, are present both in the male and in the female; hence it is questionable whether they really function, as alleged, to support the pouch. Rather do the bones serve as attachment for the muscle (the iliomarsupialis) which winds around the bones and by its contraction compresses the mammary gland and forces out the milk. Morgan claimed to have traced, in the kangaroo, muscle fibers from this muscle sheet into the nipple and around the milk ducts, thus providing, he thought, a complete mechanism for emptying the milk. That this condition is something special in the kangaroo or any other marsupial I doubt; for in all mammals there are muscle fibers throughout the gland, and every suckling young, from mouse to elephant, must work for its sustenance.

This matter has been subjected to study by modern methods. Robert K. Enders used the dual approach of anatomy and physiology. He first made careful dissections of the abdominal muscles of the opossum—all of them, not just one muscle—and their nerve supply. Then in the living, lactating female he stimulated electrically the appropriate nerves, causing the muscles to contract. Never did even a drop of milk appear at the tip of the nipples, although light squeezing with fingers or tweezers brought out the milk. The evidence is therefore unquestionably against the several-century-old "pumping" theory, which misconception we must also consign to the limbo of bad guesses.

On the positive side of the question we have direct evidence: the newborn opossum is well able to suckle. An instructive experiment was made in New South Wales by Miss Lily Irby, who removed an embryo of a marsupial, the squirrel glider, from its dead and already chilled mother and raised it on cow's milk. With its muzzle touching the milk in a teaspoon, the fetus was able to suck in the milk. Thus the act of a Good Samaritan helped to settle a scientific question. The final piece of evidence is simple enough: the sucking act of the tiny pouch young can not only be seen, it can actually be heard.

A second much-quoted misconception is that the tongue of the young grows to the nipple, organically and inseparably. This idea arose from the oft-repeated statement that the mouth of the young one bleeds when it is forcibly removed. The fact is, however, as already stated in another connection, that if it is removed by gentle traction, there is no bleeding, as my students and I have demonstrated hundreds of times. A section through the head of a pouch young with the nipple in its mouth clearly demonstrates that there positively is no fusion of tissues, or "soldering," as Geoffroy Saint-Hilaire designated the imagined condition.

A third mistaken notion has the nipple extending all the way into the stomach of the young one, like a veritable stomach tube. This it never does. But there exists in the embryo's throat an interesting arrangement whereby the creature may swallow milk and breathe at the same time. No chance for choking. The epiglottis or lid of the larynx, which must close the glottis or opening to the air passages in swallowing, is tubular in the opossum and extends up into the nasal chamber in such a way that the milk may run down into the gullet without obstructing the windpipe. Such an arrangement obtains also in certain whales. And picture the alligator lying in the shallows near the shore, with its mouth open under water and only its nostrils and malevolent eyes showing above the surface.

Just as writers of today like to fictionalize their animal stories and color them with sentimental effusions, so writers of the past have endowed the kangaroo and the opossum with the human trait of maternal love.

While the young are in the pouch and attached to the teats, I have never seen an opossum mother give any attention to them, and I have had scores of such mothers in my cages. However, I have read that kangaroo mothers have been seen to insert their muzzles into the pouch, presumably to lick the young. Troughton cites the case of the sugar glider of Australia, which has been seen holding her pouch open with her forepaws while she "carefully licked the tiny pink infants therein."

There is a story concerning the solicitude of a kangaroo mother carrying her "joey" (large kangaroo young, in the local vernacular) when close pressed by dogs. According to one version, joey is "abstracted with the mother's forepaws and thrown out into the bush." This is not a case of callous self-interest, but is done to save the baby from the dogs. George Jennison, in his *Natural History of Animals* (1927), a standard work, repeats the story with variations: "The females are much smaller than the males and more easily exhausted. When sufficiently terrified, they will cast their young ones from the pouch to effect their own escape. Many baby kangaroos are obtained in this way for zoological gardens. They are placed in baize bags and fed at first on milk and afterwards on grains and hay."

Another version taxes one's credulity even more: the mother, after casting off her burden, is pictured as fondly looking back at the place where she left her youngster so long as this is still in sight—a touching picture of

116

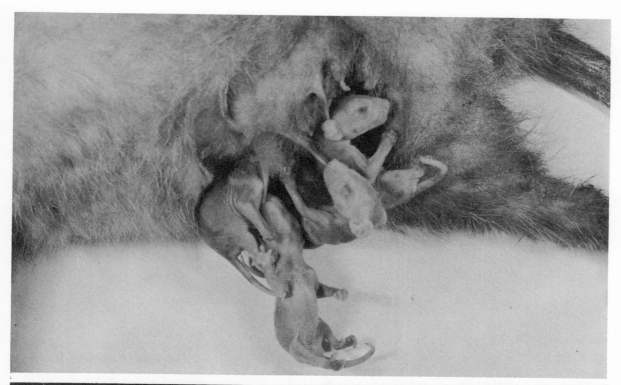

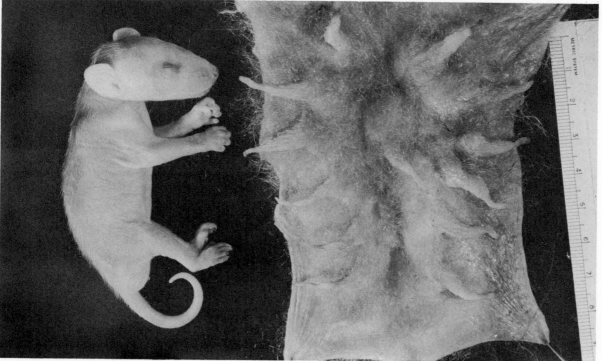

Two photographs of a most unusual case of an opossum pouch with one extra nipple, making a total of fourteen, all of which were occupied. Ithaca, New York, May 29, 1951. Courtesy W. J. Hamilton.

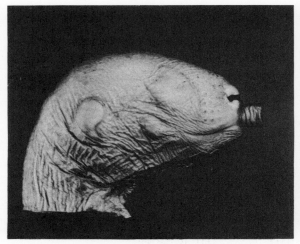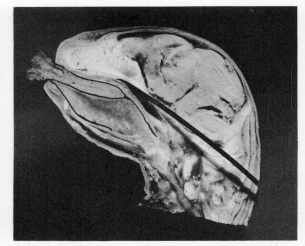

Left: head of pouch young, with nipple in mouth. Right: sagittal section, showing powerful tongue and the limited distance to which the nipple extends into the mouth. The bristle is in the respiratory passage.

maternal devotion which should make the modern behaviorist cringe.

But naturalists generally were not objective in their descriptions of animal behavior. Objectivity in this field was a later development, largely of the present century. Audubon was no exception, as the following excerpt from his *Episodes* shows:

There cannot be a better exemplification of maternal tenderness than the female Opossum. Just peep into that curious sack in which the young are concealed, each attached to a teat. The kind mother not only nourishes them with care, but preserves them from their enemies; she moves with them as the shark with her progeny, and now, aloft on the tulip-tree, she hides them away among the thick foliage. By the end of two months they begin to shift for themselves; each has been taught its particular lesson, and must now practice it.

Dr. Barton, usually quite objective in his natural history, let slip this bit of sentiment: "I have seen the mother, when the marsupium is forcibly opened to bring into view the contained embryos, manifest her distress by a kind of supplicating manner—and evidently shed tears."

Dumont de Montigny had earlier written on the opossum's motherliness in these words:

It is there [in the pouch] that, after she has brought forth, she places her young, who, clinging to her dugs, are nourished with her milk, and grow in a sure shelter, where it is always warm; upon seeing the animal in this state, one would be tempted to think that she was still with young. As soon as the young are strong enough to come out and run on the grass, the mother lets them out, so that they may fetch upon the ground some worms to feast upon. Should she hear some noise or see some suspicious movement, she utters a certain cry, and upon hearing that signal which is known to them, the little ones are seen running to their mother and entering her body from which they have issued. When one of these mothers is killed in that state, the pocket opens itself and the little ones come out. They are then rather pretty.

This account, fresh from the recently settled possessions in the New World, probably touched the hearts of the French, who avidly read it as well as Du Pratz's report from Louisiana: "The female carries them about with the utmost affection and they may frequently be seen sporting in and out of the belly." William Bingley in 1805 quoted this passage of the opossum mother's martyrdom from Du Pratz's volume: "And if we may believe du Pratz, it will not . . . yield any signs of life even though placed on a redhot iron; and when there are any young in the pouch of a female, she will suffer both herself and them to be roasted alive rather than give them up."

The prize for an essay on maternal love as exemplified by the opossum, however, should without question go to E. F. Gautier, quotations from whose *Observations sur l'histoire naturelle* were published in *Le Dictionnaire raisonné* of 1759. I have rendered into English the following heart-warming passage.

The female of this species is favored by the possession of a pouch to satisfy the extraordinary love she has for her young, which are born naked and bare, eyes closed, and consequently in need of help. The mother takes care not to lose them, caresses them ceaselessly, nourishes them, and places them into her pouch or muff to keep them warm. She carries them about with her wherever she goes without exposing them to the air or cold. She nurses them within the portable cradle at nipples ranged in the pouch for the accommodation of the young marmots, according to their needs.

The mother of exemplary tenderness makes the little ones go out from time to time, especially when it rains, in order to let them drink; she then washes them with her paws, licks them, and promptly places them back into the pouch; sometimes she suns them when the weather is fine; and when their eyes are opened, she amuses them, dances with them, bounces them, and teaches them to walk; but as soon as they are strong enough to seek their own food, she chases them out, as it were, to incite them to look after themselves; however, she follows them and watches over them from a distance; and if by chance the slightest noise betokens danger, she runs to them, takes one after another into her pouch, and carries them to a safe and quiet place; she does not quit them without a thousand caresses and a thousand playful gambols.

This makes a charming tale, which perhaps Gautier enjoyed telling his children. But the *Dictionnaire raisonné et universel des animaux* was not supposed to be a collection of bedtime stories, but rather a serious compendium of scientific information.

From these studies and others that might be cited, it is clear that the opossum pouch young is a favorable object for experimental studies in the field of growth and differentiation. When born, it is a veritable embryo and yet it is a breathing, digesting, reacting entity, outside the uterus and therefore quite accessible to the investigator. A few scientists have already made use of this subject of experimentation. Two hundred years ago, Buffon had something to say on this subject from a medical point of view: "It would be desirable to observe living *sarigues,* and more particularly to examine their precocious exclusion from the uterus. By such observations we might obtain some insight into the methods of preserving the lives of children prematurely born. The gestation of these children having been proportionately short, the period of lactation should be lengthened."

Today it still holds that any basic truth learned from animal experimentation will eventually redound, sometimes by most circuitous routes, to the growth of medical science and the benefit of mankind.

17

Opossum and Bear

As a subject of animal legendry the opossum is rivaled by the bear. In early records of the life history of both of these animals, fable was substituted for fact because of the lack of accurate knowledge concerning the birth and neonatal care of the young. This paucity of information was due to the difficulties of making the necessary observations. The she-bear "dens up" in winter, going into partial hibernation in a convenient cave or other hollow protected against the weather. There she gives birth to her young. Since the bear cubs are born in such seclusion, all that was popularly known about them was that they were, in comparison with the young of the familiar domestic animals, of absurdly small size. Consequently there arose about them a legend which can be traced back two millennia, long before the opossum mother and her young began to acquire their aura of mystery.

Bear and opossum, unlike as they are, have one trait in common: the relative weights of mother and newborn offspring find their extreme in these two forms of animal life.

The weight of the newborn opossum is somewhat variable, if one accepts the figures of different investigators. Barton weighed a litter of seven: one weighed scarcely 1 grain (one seven-thousandth of a pound), another

barely 2 grains, and the remaining five together exactly 7, an average of 1.43 grains. Audubon and Bachman came into possession of a female that had three young in the pouch weighing 2.5, 3.5, and 3.75 grains, and they removed one by Caesarian section which weighed 4 grains—an average for the litter of 3.4 grains. Dr. Meigs weighed one of a litter of thirteen on what was probably the second day after birth; its weight was 3.5 grains. Dr. Carl Moore's well-controlled figures for four one-day-old pouch young, each from a different litter, were 2, 2.25, 2.1, and 2.8 grains respectively. One three-day-old young weighed 3.75, a four-day-old 4.8 grains. On the basis of these figures I should be inclined to consider 2.5 grains approximately correct for the newborn young of the Virginia opossum. As there are 437.5 grains in an ounce, one ounce of opossums would number about 175 young ones, instead of 270, as I previously published the figure.

What, then, is the ratio of the baby's weight to that of the mother? Opossums breed when no heavier than 900 grams, or about 2 pounds; old breeding females may weigh up to 6 pounds and occasionally more; a good average may be set at 1,350 grams, or 3 pounds. There being 7,000 grains in a pound and a newborn opossum weighing 2.5

grains, the ratio is 1:8,400; i.e., the average mother weighs 8,400 times as much as one of her offspring. If, however, we base our calculations on the combined weight of a litter of say twenty, the ratio of litter weight to that of the mother comes to only 1:420.

This is a very low ratio as compared with the giant kangaroo. A female of 180 pounds gives birth to a single baby no larger than the two end joints of a child's finger. George Morse weighed one which he saw born; it weighed 19.5 grains. A 180-pound kangaroo mother could weigh 60,000 times as much as her single offspring. She has no close competitors in this field.

Data on a modest contender, the bear, are hard to get, but I have collected a few reliable figures, especially those from Dr. Francis G. Benedict, formerly director of the Nutrition Laboratory of the Carnegie Institution. He had the good fortune to acquire a bear fetus. The fetus weighed 14 ounces; and as the mother was a 400-pound grizzly (the father an 1,100-pound Alaskan brown bear), the ratio of the cub to its mother was 1:457 (to the father 1:1,257). The mammalogist C. Hart Merriam sent me the following figures: one grizzly female which weighed 390 pounds had a cub somewhat over 9 ounces in weight:

ratio, 1:625. Brehm's *Tierleben* cites a polar bear cub weighing 1.7 pounds; if the mother weighed 1,500 pounds, we would have a ratio of 1:880. The figures would have to be halved if the calculation were based on litter, i.e., combined twin weights, for bears usually give birth to twins, occasionally to triplets, rarely to quadruplets.

In drawing comparisons with other mammals, one may cite these ratios: 1:16 for man, 1:25 for dog pup, and 1:30 for some members of the deer family.

While we are on the subject of baby-mother ratios, it might be well to remind ourselves of the other extreme, in which the baby's weight begins to approach that of the mother, as in the case of the bat. From the bat *Nyctinomus mexicanus,* which gives birth to a single young a year, I have removed many a fetus near term which weighed one-third as much as the female carrying it; this corresponds to a forty-pound human baby. Sherman watched a mother Myotis weighing 7.25 grams give birth to two young weighing respectively 1.10 and 1.15 grams, a ratio of 1:3. Somehow Nature grants to the small bat relatively huge babies, and small babies to the huge bear.

This very disproportion in size of the bear

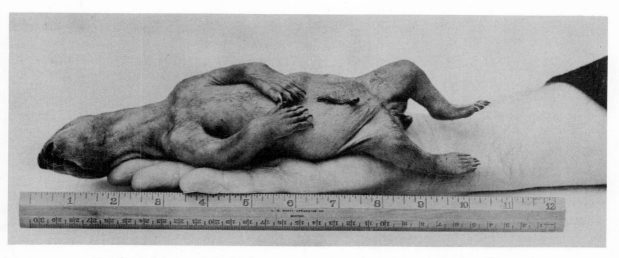

Newborn bear, weight fourteen ounces. Courtesy Francis G. Benedict.

cub to that of the mother makes it a favorable subject about which to weave a legend. There is an age-old and widespread legend of how the bear cub is born a formless mass of flesh, devoid of face or limbs, which the mother bear must lick into shape.

Before the end of the first century, Pliny the Elder had put the story into the only work of his that has survived, his *Historia naturalis*, a storehouse of the folklore and superstitions of his age. He compiled everything unquestioningly, uninhibited by scientific skepticism, rare in his time. Natural history was not presented by Pliny as an accurate science, but rather as a vehicle for moralizing. The stories read entertainingly and served their purpose for centuries. Even in the seventeenth century Pliny's "Storybook of Nature," as I prefer to call it, was recommended by Milton as a textbook for the schools. Here is Pliny's version of the bear story:

The she-bear gives birth in its cave in the thirtieth week, some time after June 5. The newborn young are pale, formless pieces of flesh, somewhat larger than mice, without eyes or hair, only the claws are visible. By virtue of the mother's licking they gradually assume shape. . . . There is nothing rarer than to see a bear in labor.

As Pliny was primarily a compiler, it is hardly likely that the legend originated with him. Indeed, his contemporaries Plutarch and Petronius alluded to it, as did Virgil, who in his *Aeneid*, written just before the Christian Era, applied the tale to Romulus and Remus:

By the wolf were laid the martial twins
Intrepid on her swelling dugs they hung.
The foster-dam lolled out her fawning tongue;
They sucked secure, while bending back her head
  She licked their tender limbs and formed them
    as they fed.

The legend enjoyed an extensive distribution. The following Arabian version is taken from Kazwini's *Arabian Kosmographia:*

When the female bear is about to give birth she **seeks a black stone** which has been struck by

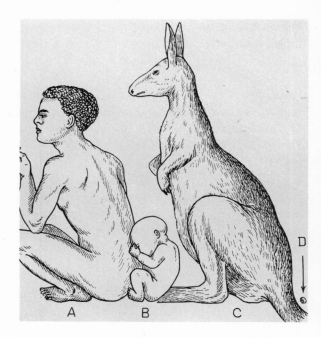

Nature's contrasts: A, *adult man;* B, *newborn child;* C, *adult kangaroo;* D, *newborn kangaroo. Drawn to scale. Courtesy H. C. Raven and* Natural History.

lightning, for this makes parturition easier. Failing to find such a stone she accomplishes the same object by taking up a position opposite the constellation of Ursus Minor or the Little Bear. At birth the newborn young is like a piece of flesh, without form; she does not give up licking until the shapes of the limbs become clearly visible. Every hour she carries her young from place to place to prevent its being destroyed by swarms of ants. But after the limbs have grown strong she remains quietly in one place, occasionally laying her offspring down to suckle a hyena. This has given rise to the Arabic saying: "So-and-so is more stupid than the bear mother."

And so through the centuries the weird tale persisted. In 1600 there was published an edition of one of Joachim Camerarius' works which bore a picture of a bear licking a shapeless cub. Since Camerarius was a scholarly churchman and only secondarily a naturalist, his mistake is excusable. Similar errors on the part of professed scientists in the more enlightened centuries are less easy to understand. Brickell, for example, published this item in his early book on the natural history of Virginia:

They have commonly three to five cubs at a time, without hair or eyes, only there is some appearance of Claws. This rude Lump they fashion by degrees, by their constant licking. [Shades of Pliny here!] It is likewise reported that after conception they will sleep so soundly for fourteen Days that it is not possible to awaken them, and that during their abode in those secret Places, they never appear abroad for Food, but only suck their Paws, which is all they subsist on during that time.

Various poets have told the story, each in his own way, of which several samples follow. Poetic license justifies them; versifiers are privileged to warp truth for the sake of metaphor, especially when they use the figure as a vehicle for a spiritual message.

Brings forth a thing that's indigest
A lump of flesh without all fashion,
Which she, by often licking, brings to rest,
Making a formal body, good and sound,
Which often in this island we have found.
CHESTER, *Love's Martyr*

A bear's a savage beast, of all
Most ugly and unnatural;
Whelp'd, without form, until the dam
Has lick'd it into shape and frame.
BUTLER, *Hudibras*

The cubs of bears a living lump appear
When whelp'd, and no determined figure
wear,
The mother licks them into shape, and gives
As much of form as she herself receives.
DRYDEN

There arose dissenters who refused to accept the story of the unformed cub. In the fourth century B.C., Aristotle, teacher of Alexander the Great, wrote more objectively than his predecessors, selecting those parts of the bear story that he considered truth. As Ashton quotes Aristotle: "The she-bear carries her young 30 weeks and gives birth to one or two or at most five young. The newborn is very small in comparison to the size of the mother; it is smaller than a weasel, somewhat larger than a mouse, naked and blind and its limbs for the most part unjointed."

Kurt Elze, whose researches have guided me in this subject, has pointed out that Aristotle said nothing about the licking process. Albertus Magnus, popularizer of Aristotle's works on natural history, denied the story. Teacher and colleague of Thomas Aquinas, he was a great churchman, yet a distinguished authority on natural science. Four centuries later, Aldrovandi had in his museum in Bologna an actual specimen of a bear fetus, which in 1642 his pupil Ambrosini described and illustrated in order to combat the spread of the baseless item of so-called "natural history." About the same time Sir Thomas Browne, physician, scientist, and author, in his *Pseudodoxia epidemica* or *Inquiry into Vulgar Errors*, blasted the idea of the legend in these words, quoted from F. Edward Hulme:

[The legend] is not only repugnant unto the sense of everyone that shall enquire into it, but of exact and deliberate experiment. It is, moreover, injurious unto reason and much impugneth the course and providence of nature to conceive a birth should be ordained before there is a formation. Besides, what few take notice of, men do hereby in a high measure vilify the works of God, imputing that unto the tongue of a Beast.

This has the finality of an amen. At the end of the eighteenth century Pennant relinquished belief in the story, albeit halfheartedly, for men often give up deep-rooted ideas only under pressure. His contemporary, the anatomist Blumenbach, tried to change the prevailing false notion, but in vain, for it had become so fixed as a tradition that it is reflected even today in our vernacular. The popular mind imagined that a bear cub, neglected by its dam, would be a misshapen, blundering, helpless boob of a bear. Hence "unlicked" came to mean in the vernacular, when applied to a person, a boorish, ill-bred yokel. The Brothers Grimm, German philologists and mythologists, spoke of their rude, unlicked fellow-countrymen. In *King Henry VI*, Shakespeare refers to Gloucester thus:

> Like to a chaos, or an unlick'd bear-whelp
> That carries no impression like the dam.

Charles Kingsley in *Yeast* also uses the figure:

> . . . Alas poor Lancelot! An
> Unlicked bear, with all his sorrows.

The allusion to the unlicked bear has been used by authors from Virgil on, to express despair of reaching perfection in their works. The poet Wieland wrote: "I shall not tire to lick my born bears and make them acceptable, if possible." In *The Anatomy of Melancholy*, best seller for two hundred years, Burton makes Democritus Junior tell the reader: "I must for that cause do my business myself, as a bear doth with her whelps, to bring forth this confused lump; I had not time to lick it into form, as she doth her young ones." And Pope in the *Dunciad:*

> So watchful Bruin forms with plastic care
> Each growing lump, and brings it to a bear.

The bear cub even became a symbol in art, for Titian is said to have used it to indicate that in many cases art is more significant than nature.

The legend of the bear cub and its dam has also been used to emphasize spiritual development. According to this injunction, every individual must work on his own soul, gradually bringing it to perfection. As an example of this idea I have attempted to translate, keeping both the prosody and the childlike simplicity, the poem "Renner," by Hugo Von Tremberg, written in 1300:

> Old scribes assure us that the bear
> Instead of young throws flesh quite rare,
> Which licked with mother's tender tongue
> Soon takes the form of Bruin's young;
> The whelp, though born a midget small,
> Yet great will grow in limbs and all,
> Once licked into a creature whole.
> Who is concerned about his soul
> Should lay aside the will to sin
> With which his heart is taken in
> And with the tongue of penitence
> Lick it until he gain the sense
> Of virtuous works, before denied,
> Now by His Grace thrice multiplied.

18

A Butterfly Painter Starts a Legend

Very early in the history of Dutch settlements in South America, Maria Sibylla Merian lived in Dutch Guiana, where she had come with her daughter in 1699 to paint the gorgeous tropical butterflies; but her last drawing was that of an opossum, and this started a legend.

Madame Merian was descended from a family of artists, among whom was the engraver Johann Theodor de Bry, her maternal grandfather. Through him the granddaughter had come by her interest in opossums naturally, for he had made beautiful copper engravings of that animal in several of his famous books of travel. De Bry, a Huguenot, had fled with his family and belongings from Liége and settled in Frankfurt, where he set up a publishing house.

About the same time there came to Frankfurt from Basle, Switzerland, one Matthew Merian, also a copper engraver, who soon married De Bry's daughter, the mother of Maria. The talented Maria painted miniatures, but her real interest was in plants and insects. Armed with a Gesner and an Aldrovandi, standard zoology texts of the day, she traveled to Surinam, where she collected notes and made sketches for her book. This now rare folio volume was published after her death by her daughter Dorothea.

It is the last of the copper plates in this book that especially interests us, in spite of one critic's opinion that "the closing plate presents a heterogeneous assemblage of various objects disposed in a most fanciful manner and is absolutely worthless." I reproduce the plate here because it started a bit of nature-faking that has lasted to the present day —over two hundred years. It concerns a certain way in which the mother opossum is supposed to carry her young.

Madame Merian explains how the opossum got into her insect book. On the last plate she had filled the upper half with a tree trunk against which she sketched a male and a female praying mantis—so why not draw in the foreground a likeness of that strange new beast, the opossum? The species selected, called by her *Boschrot* or *rat de forêt,* is now known as *Didelphis dorsigera* or Merian's opossum. *Dorsigera* is Latin for "back-carrier."

The pertinent feature of the picture is the very neat manner in which the young opossums' tails are wrapped around that of the mother. The artist added the following verbal description: "When the mother goes out in search of food, the young follow and when they have eaten or are in a state of fear they jump on the mother's back, twist their tails about hers, and she carries them thus to her nest."

The picture that started a tradition. Above: life history of the praying mantis. Below: mother Didelphis dorsigera with young on her back, their tails wrapped around her tail. From Maria Merian's *Insects of Surinam (1717).*

126

The nineteenth-century "improvement" on Maria Merian's original drawing of a mother opossum carrying her young. Left: from J. G. Wood's Handy Natural History *(1886). Right: from G. R. Waterhouse's* Marsupialia *(1846).*

So the cute little dorsigeras and their co-operating dam were introduced to the world.

Linnaeus used Madame Merian's description almost verbatim: "Dorsigera. Inhabits Surinam; burrows in the ground; brings five or six young, which when in danger stick to the back of the mother, twisting their tails around hers."

Pennant also repeats this passage. Blu-

menbach incorporated the story in his popular handbook of nature study and referred to this opossum as the "Surinam Aeneas"—not too good an allusion, for was it not the father whom Aeneas carried on his back, while he led his son Ascanius by the hand? Bingley, who popularized the "manners and economy of animal creation" in England at the beginning of last century, included the details of

 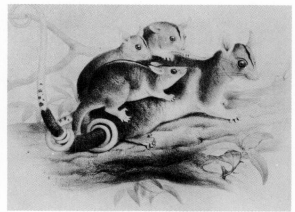

Left: J. Smit's drawing of Didelphis azarae *made for Hudson's* Naturalist in La Plata *(1892). This was doubtless copied from Alston's illustration of* Didelphis derbiana *(right) in* Biologia centrali americana *(1870–82). The poses of the young as they cling to their mother's back are more or less in keeping with the original drawing of Maria Merian.*

127

A heavily laden mother.

Merian's opossum in his *Animal Biography*.

Early in the present century, Lottridge in his *Familiar Wild Animals* published his own version of tail-about-tail transport, which was promptly copied by the author of *Mammals of America* in "Nature Lover's Library." The habit in question in these essays no longer referred to Merian's opossum only, but was attached to the Virginia opossum as well: "Sometimes the mother arches her tail over her back very much after the fashion of a squirrel, and the little ones cling to it by their prehensile tails, and feet touching her back, presenting a curious sight indeed."

The reader will notice that now the mother arches her tail over her back; and not only that—the young hang suspended therefrom. Perfectly astounding! That compelling mod-ern writer on natural history, Alan Devoe, in his *Speaking of Animals* accepts Lottridge's addition to Merian's description, changing the wording but little. The young, he says, "snuggle into the fur on the back as external passengers. Now and again, when she arches her tail, squirrel fashion, over her back, they wrap the tips of their own tails around hers and hang upside down."

Who first added the new wrinkle of the arching tail to Mother Dorsigera's behavior and technique, I do not know, but the idea did not originate with Lottridge. The earliest case I have run across is the otherwise acceptable plate of marsupial animals which an artist drew for Oliver Goldsmith's well-known *History of the Earth and Animated Nature*. At the right in this figure is pictured

128

an opossum, wrongly labeled murine, with young attached to the mother's tail, very delicately, by their own. Two other drawings will serve to demonstrate the wide acceptance of the dorsal presentation of the mother's tail. J. G. Wood had his artists, the Dalziel brothers, sketch Dorsigera in all its glory in his *Illustrated Natural History,* and Waterhouse had the same pose perpetuated in his volume on marsupials in the *Naturalist's Library.*

In more recent literature the opossum still has her tail elevated. Krieg, writing in 1924 on Metachirus and Didelphis, says: "The young dig their claws deep into the fur of the mother, anchoring themselves by their tails to the elevated tail of the dam." The mammalogist Witmer Stone had given a still more vivid description some years before: "When six or eight inches long they may often be seen swarming over the back of their parent, their naked tails twisted around hers, or hanging head down with her from some horizontal limb."

One would naturally like to see a photograph of this striking phenomenon, to prove its genuineness. I have searched for such a photograph and actually found one on page 380, Volume II, of the *Library of Natural History,* by W. Saville-Kent, only to discover that the photograph was posed by a stuffed specimen in which the taxidermist must cer-

tainly have stiffened the mother's tail with a steel wire.

The truth is that all opossums carry their young on their backs from the time that they become too large for the pouch. The young hold on to the thick fur of their dam by means of stout claws; they grasp her fur anywhere—on neck, head, back, or legs—not merely over her shoulders to "preserve the total center of gravity," as Lippincott would have the juvenile readers of his *Persimmon Jim, the 'Possum* believe. The youngsters' tails are not idle in these situations, but are wrapped about any available part of the mother's anatomy, which happens very often to be her tail. Several pictures reproduced in this book amply illustrate the point; and a number of writers of books on natural history have had their artists draw the arrangement correctly, as Hudson's illustration of *Didelphis azarae* and the one that Alston had sketched of the same species in the London Zoological Gardens. In the recent literature on the natural history of mammals there are many reproductions of photographs which practically duplicate my own shown here.

The facts of nature are thrilling enough without embellishment. What could be more appealing than a family of opossums riding around on their mother's back, or a koala youngster pig-a-back, or a yearling kangaroo still welcome in its mother's expanded pouch?

19

Four Centuries of Opossum Pictures

IN THIS CHAPTER I have assembled representative illustrations of the opossum to
supplement those already used to embellish
earlier chapters. The total collection reveals
the development of animal picturization, with
the opossum as subject.

In the following table are listed, in chrono-
logical order, marsupial pictures of four centuries, most of them reproduced in this book.
Also listed are the materials employed in
making the blocks or plates from which the
pictures were printed. Four hundred years
of changes, covering almost the entire age of
printing, are recorded as new media were
adapted to the art of line engraving: wood,
copper, steel, and stone.

Date	Technique	Author
1516	Wood	Waldseemüller
1522	Wood	Ptolemy
1551	Wood	Gesner
1563	Wood	Gesner–Forer
1557	Wood	Stade
1558	Wood	Thevet
1590	Copper	Harriot–De Bry
1604	Copper	De Bry
1657	Copper	Johnston–Merian
1658	Copper	Rochefort
1698	Copper	De Bruyn
1717	Copper	Merian
1737	Copper	Brickell
1749	Steel	Buffon
1763	Wood	Du Pratz
1773	Steel	Hawkesworth
1790	Wood	Bewick
1792	Copper	Kerr
1823	Copper	Goldsmith
1824	Lithograph	G. Saint-Hilaire–Cuvier
1831	Steel	Godman
1846	Lithograph	Waterhouse
1851	Lithograph	Audubon and Bachman
1867	Wood	Tenney
1867	Wood	La Fontaine–Dore
1879	Lithograph	Alston
1886	Wood	Wood
1887	Lithograph	Selenka
1892	Lithograph	Hudson

*Opossum effigy "platform" pipe, from Temple
Mound, Scioto County, Ohio. About natural
size. Here published for the first time, courtesy H. C. Shetrone, formerly director of the
Ohio State Archaeological Society.*

130

The first woodcut of the opossum was made seventy years after the invention of the process and sixteen years after the animal was introduced to the Old World. The first picture of the opossum made from a copper engraving we owe to that pioneer in the art, De Bry (1590 and 1604). The earliest steel engraving which is represented in the list is a sample of the beautiful illustrations used by Buffon in the middle of the eighteenth century in his world-famous *Natural History*. Buffon's worthy successors in the field of zoology, Geoffroy Saint-Hilaire and Cuvier, took advantage of the more accurate, newly invented method of printing from stone. Other illustrations in this book are done by the modern method of photographic engraving: on zinc for plain line drawings, on copper for halftones.

By way of wood, copper, steel, stone, and sensitized plate, the opossum has been pictured from Colonial days to the present. Flash bulbs have caught Mother Possum in her night ambles; the motion-picture screen has brought her into the theater and classroom; television doubtless will bring her into the living room.

The first series of pictures includes the work of the white man from western Europe; this is followed by the very creditable prehistoric drawings and sculpturing from primitive cultures—Aztec, Mayan, Australian, and our own pre-Columbian Mound Builders—but regrettably nothing from our post-Columbian red men.

Long before the discovery of the New World the Aztecs of Mexico and the Mayans of Central America had developed a high degree of culture. A phenomenon so unusual as the abdominal pouch of the female opossum could not have escaped the eye of these keen observers.

In another connection I have presented an essentially correct if very simple drawing of the female opossum with young looking out of the pouch. This was sketched from the

Two centuries of opossum pictures. Top to bottom: Hans Stade's serwoy (1557); Johnston's carigueya (1657), about the same as Nierembergius' illustration (1635); Rochefort's opassum (1658), which he took from Piso and Marcgrave (1648); and Du Pratz's rat de bois (1763). Du Pratz's and Stade's are woodcuts, the others copper engravings.

131

Copper engraving by the elder De Bry, from the series of Voyages *published by him and his two sons between 1590 and 1634. This picture of a Brazilian landscape was published in 1604.*

Florentine Codex of Aztec manuscripts. It is quite natural that the Aztecs should have known the opossum as they did other native species, for Montezuma had a zoological garden that won the admiration of their Spanish conquerors.

Of similar Mayan pictures I find none; but that these people recognized the peculiar mode of reproduction seems indicated by the fact that the animal was one of their totems, for it represented the god of fertility and the female element in nature, as the coyote represented the male. The opossum also had something to do with the nether regions. In the highly conventionalized drawings of the Mayans, the identifying character is the black eyespot, which is conspicuously developed in the Central American *Didelphis mesamericana*. There would seem to be little doubt that the sketches shown were inspired by the opossum.

Art objects representing the opossum were prevalent in widely separated geographical regions of Central America. Seler cites, for example, the ceramics of Cholula and the pottery of Michoacán; but I have not personally

132

Above: steel engravings from Buffon (1749). La sarigue (Didelphis marsupialis) *and pouchless marmosa. Below: woodcut from Bewick (1790).*

Male (below) and female opossum, from Geoffroy Saint-Hilaire and F. Cuvier (1824). These lithographs are sufficiently lifelike for one to identify the Virginia opossum as such.

seen any of these in the image of the opossum or of any other animal. Neither have I been able to find any such works of art by the North American Indian. On his travels in Colombia, Dr. R. K. Enders found that the Indians there still show golden effigies of the opossum, in which the hollowed-out pouch encloses a pebble, the whole figure functioning somewhat as a bell.

Within the confines of the United States, in the valley of the Mississippi, particularly in Ohio and Indiana, skillful artists flourished

among the Mound Builders long before these people were supplanted by the modern Amerinds. These artists were sculptors, who fashioned ceremonial pipes, many made in the image of animals. Some of the pipes are of the so-called "platform" type described by Edwin A. Barber as follows:

Steel engraving of an opossum family from John D. Godman's American Natural History *(1846). Male, on the ground, and female with large pouch young. This picture is correct except for the tenuous hold one young has on the twig above.*

Lithograph of Virginia opossum, from a painting by John James Audubon for Audubon's and Bachman's The Quadrupeds of North America *(1851).*

Woodcut from Tenney's Natural History *(1867). This sketch was also used in the* International Dictionary, *first edition.*

Not only are the features of the animals represented faithfully, but their peculiarities and habits are in some degree exhibited. In one pipe we recognize the otter with a fish in his mouth. The tufted heron is seen in the position of devouring a fish. Nothing can surpass the truthfulness and delicacy of the sculpture. The minutest feathers are shown; the articulations of the legs of the birds, also the gills, fins and scales of the fish, are represented. The hawk is shown in the act of tearing a small bird. The beaver also figures in the collection, as also do the bear, panther, wolf, wildcat, elk, opossum and squirrel; the buzzard, crow, eagle, falcon, owl, raven, duck, grouse, parroquet and swallow; the serpent [rattlesnake], turtle, frog, toad and a number of other animals which have been readily recognized. The sockets of the eyes in the majority of the bird pipes were set with pearls from clams of the local streams.

One of these, made of Ohio pipestone, is an opossum pipe, possibly the only whole one in existence. The platform measures 3.5 inches in length. The opossum may be recognized by the shape of the snout, the eyes (which are set with copper), and the scaly tail. One foot is represented as if inserted in a hole in search of food. The perforation of the platform begins at the left of the illustration.

Just as the story of the opossum is unfolded in the sequence and evolution of animal illustrating, so, too, it can be traced through the ledgers of historians and *voyageurs*. The opossum has been the subject of progressive studies in zoology, anatomy, and physiology.

135

It is featured in the records of hunters and trappers and conservationists. It has been a challenge to furriers and to cooks. And last but not least, Br'er Possum has been rambling persistently through the folklore of the four and one-half centuries which have witnessed the world-wide expansion of the nations of western Europe.

A figure from the Nuttall Codex, edited by Eduard Seler. Again, the characteristic eyespot is present; one may also read "opossum" in the tail and the opposable thumb and the great toe.

Plate from Eduard Seler's Animal Pictures of the Mexican and the Mayan Manuscripts. *The characteristic feature by which each figure may be identified as the opossum is the black eyespot.*

20

Possum Hunting

Possum hunting is indigenous to the South, where from the Ozarks to the Everglades nearly every farm home has its quota of possum hounds. These are rarely purebred hounds but mostly mongrels of poorly defined ancestry, yet with a good remnant, from aristocratic ancestors, of sad eyes, heavy jowl, long pendant ears, and deep voice. Intelligence and adaptability in dogs are no more a monopoly of family relationship than in the human species. While it is possible to breed disposition and adaptability into a race of dogs by ruthless selection, as the Seeing Eye organization has done for the German shepherd, it is also possible for a practiced dog connoisseur to step into a populous pound and pick out, with uncanny certainty, a dog which will prove trainable for a particular task. This is just what the master of many a possum hound has done.

A possum trailer, purebred or mongrel, must be trained to the task, like any canine specialist. Such training requires time and skill, several years perhaps, with much practice in the closed season. When live prey is not available, an old skin suffices to mark the trail. The skin is dragged over the ground and, perhaps hours later, the hounds are turned loose to follow the trail. A possum dog must learn to respond only to possum scent.

If Fido comes to a point where a cottontail rabbit has run across the trail and he veers off to pursue it, he is punished and set right, for possum only must be followed, never rabbit, raccoon, skunk, or any other game abroad at the time; otherwise he is not a "possum dog."

Possum hunting is a social institution. You almost never hunt alone; you make it a neighborhood affair to which each member brings his dog or dogs, and a merry party it usually is. A chorus of hounds barking in the glen is jollier than a single call. Besides, in the primitiveness of the dark woods and fields, whether you believe in "hants" or not, there is great satisfaction in human company. This must seem especially so to the invited tenderfoot from the city who steps from the bright lights into the mysterious darkness of field and stream. A good time is assured all; and one wonders whether the red-caparisoned riders bounding after the foxhounds have any more fun. Possum hunting gets into the blood in the same way that fox hunting is reputed to do. But for the possum hunt neither silver spurs nor scarlet coat is needed; the capital investment is so slight that every share-cropper may indulge in the sport in the nearest river bottom. Indeed, as Lewis Nordyke, writing in the July, 1948, *Sports Afield*, aptly says,

Governor Franklin D. Roosevelt of New York on a possum hunt at White Sulphur Springs, Georgia, November 29, 1930. He is here shown (in car) surrounded by a group of possum hunters, with their dogs, lantern, flashlight, and, of course, the possum in the tree. Wide World Photos, Inc.

the possum is a hard-times animal, the "pore man's varmint." Nevertheless, as the photograph here reproduced proves, the sport was enjoyed by no less a person than Franklin Delano Roosevelt when he was governor of New York.

You may, of course, in this day and time, equip yourself a little more elaborately than in the olden times, substituting a four-battery flashlight for a pine torch or a kerosene lantern with which to locate a possum in a tree by "shining" his eyes. A twenty-two rifle also makes the recovery of the animal, once it is treed, a little easier.

The opportune time for the hunt is on a night when the moon is waxing, for this is said to bring good luck; and for still better luck, wait till after dark to light the lanterns. The hunt, like the possum itself, has its traditions and superstitions.

Nine times out of ten the rendezvous is somewhere in a wooded bottom, near a stream, the favorite habitat of the possum, where he makes his nightly rounds following his accustomed trail. It is late in autumn when the open season for game begins. In the field the frost is on the ground, the persimmons and papaws are ripe, and possums are prime.

When all is ready and the hounds have had their sniff of possum skin, they are unleashed and immediately scatter in the darkness. All is still; you sit about the fire and listen. There

138

Two young possums treed by accomplished possum dogs. Photograph by Underwood & Underwood.

Their tree felled, these possums are ready for their rendezvous with taters. Photograph by Underwood & Underwood.

139

Moonlight prowler.

is no need to follow the hounds, even though this is possible, for the behavior pattern of the hunted is well known. Varmints followed by dogs travel in a circle, several miles in diameter in the case of the wildcat, much less in the case of the opossum. The progress of the hounds is punctuated by an occasional bark while they are hot on the trail, thus keeping you posted on their progress as you sit back and enjoy the warmth and glow of the fire.

Once the possum is flushed, the end of the trail is not far off. Not that he is often caught by dogs on the ground. When pursuers get too close, he dives into a den in the ground or more often climbs a convenient tree; or maybe the trail is old and leads to the persimmon tree where he has already been gorging himself. In any event, once the game is treed, a chorus, sweet to the hunters' ears, begins. Each dog sets up its own peculiar howl which means "We've got 'im treed," and each master knows his own dog's message;

but you mustn't ask him to tell you how—you must hear it for yourself, often.

Many possums caught with the aid of trained dogs find their way into the cooking pot, but many also into the fur trade. However, the bulk of the latter are still caught in spring traps, as are other wild fur bearers, such as skunks, raccoons, mink, and marten. Muskrats, too, are similarly trapped, but the muskrat industry has attained the more humane status of using traps which pull the captive under water, where it quickly drowns.

For culinary purposes opossums caught in traps are not considered so tasty as those pulled out of a 'simmon tree. The difference is probably not entirely imaginary or due to the psychological preparation of the hunt the night before; for traumatic injury, such as a crushed leg, brings about bodily changes which might well affect the flavor of the flesh, making it subtly different and less palatable, though not necessarily unfit for human consumption.

140

21

Possum Capes and Red Garters

WHILE THE SPANIARDS plundered the Aztecs and the Incas of their gold and deprived them of their independence, the French, following the English, were infiltrating the fields and forests of the North for another kind of riches—beaver fur. As Constance Skinner has vividly and romantically told us in her *Beaver, Kings and Cabins,* the trappers or *coureurs de bois* paddled their canoes up the St. Lawrence, over the Great Lakes, and down the Ohio, the Illinois, and the Mississippi rivers. The French were well established in this territory long before Daniel Boone led colonists into the fertile fields west of the Alleghenies. The English, also, were quick to recognize the value of the "cash crop" of the wilderness, the fur of beaver, wolverine, mink, and buffalo. It soon became obvious that there was not enough fur to satisfy both the French and the English, so a struggle for supremacy was inevitable. This long struggle ended in 1763 with the Treaty of Paris at the close of the French and Indian Wars.

While the contest for the North American continent had actually begun over the beaver, the larger issues of colonial expansion of the rival nations soon overshadowed the economic issues of the fur trade. As a result the beaver's true role in shaping the history of

our country has been all but overlooked. Certainly he does not figure importantly in our school textbooks.

While the beaver played so large a role for several centuries, no one ever thought of fighting over the opossum. The early settlers thought little of its hide. Captain John Smith sent some opossum pelts to England on one occasion; but because of the comparatively inferior quality of this material, it is not probable that the colonists ever made subsequent shipments. Lawson (1714) wrote that the opossum's fur "is not esteemed nor used save that Indians spin it into Girdles and Garters." Brickell (1737), plagiarist that he was, paraphrased this to say: "Their Furr is not esteemed and therefore made little use of, only that the Indians spin it into Girdles and Garters." The statement became a cliché. Even as late as 1861 the German writer of popular natural history, Fitzinger, copied this, saying: "In Louisiana women spin it into girdles and garters." I have come across this so often that I have begun to wonder whether Indian women wore anything else.

Some years after the founding of New Orleans in 1718, Dumont de Montigny could report no use being made of opossum hides: "The skin of these animals is not thought much of," he states, and he ought to have known, having represented the strictly commercial Compagnie des Indes in Louisiana for twenty-five years. Du Pratz, more of a naturalist than De Montigny, also writing from New Orleans, reported: "The *rat de bois* has a gray pelt, which though very fine, yet is never smooth. The women among the natives spin it and make garters, which they dye red."

Neither De Montigny nor Du Pratz could have foreseen that a century and a half later the environs of New Orleans would deliver annually to the fur trade a quarter of a million dollars' worth of opossum pelts to be made into decorative fur, probably none into garters and girdles.

The utilization of the opossum fur in any considerable quantity is a recent development that had to await the advancement of techniques in the fur industry as well as the vastly increased demand for fur. Improvements have resulted in both better dressing and dyeing of the less desirable pelts, which may now even be treated to simulate the rarer and more durable furs. In the scale of durability the opossum fur ranks approximately as follows:

Wolverine	100	Raccoon (dyed)	50
Otter	100	Opossum	37
Beaver	85	Mink (dyed)	35
Skunk	70	Mole	7
Mink (natural)	70	Rabbit	5
Raccoon	65		

The opossum belongs to the group of mammals that has two types of hair: underfur and overhair. The former is fine and close, gray below, with black tips. The overhairs are long and coarse and protect the coat against abrasion; they are black with tips of white in the gray phase, all black in the black phase. Skins with overhair removed, the fine underfur remaining, may, when properly dyed, be made to simulate mink. With overhair left in, a silver fox simulation is possible, the tips of the hairs being either protected against the dye so as to preserve their "silvery" whiteness or else dyed with the skin and then reversed to the original white color. Another simulation has been a combination of dyeing and blending to make the fur look like cross fox, and such skins have in the past been made into jackets and short capes. Raccoon simulations have not found favor because of the expense of the requisite fancy dyeing and the inferior quality and relative low value of the final product.

In the past the public, innocent of fur quality and unable to identify the animal species from which a given garment was made, was often defrauded by the fur merchant. Muskrat was sold for seal, rabbit for nutria, marmot or muskrat for mink, and white rabbit, even, for ermine. Today this is changed, largely under the influence of legitimate fur dealers. Your garment, if made from cheaper and inferior fur, must be labeled with some designation identifying the donor species as well as the species which it is intended to imitate, as, for example, skunkwallaby, sable-coney (rabbit), seal-musquash (muskrat), and beaver-opossum.

The importance of the opossum in the fur market of the present may be gauged by the numbers taken for the trade. While of inferior quality, the opossum still ranks eighth in the aggregate value of its fur because of the great numbers used.

As a basis for an estimate of the actual numbers involved, one may first consult the United States Fish and Wildlife leaflet, "Annual Fur Catch in the United States," issued in February, 1950, by Frank G. Ashbrook, veteran student of world resources in furs. This compilation is based on reports from departments of natural resources of the individual states, and these are as reliable as the vagaries of the state laws and the accidents of practical state politics permit. The ideal law requires that the fur dealer report his purchases; some states place the responsibility on the fur trapper, requiring him to report

One gray opossum (top), two cinnamon-colored mutations, and one albinotic. The cinnamon individual on the wire cloth lacks the stiff overhairs. The iris of the eyes of the cinnamon specimens is also cinnamon. Photograph by J. M. Kuehne.

his catch. Because of laxity in state reports there are important omissions in the summary. For instance, neither Delaware nor New Jersey is represented for the years 1944–48. Other figures are clearly unreliable: Florida reported only 4,102, South Carolina 4,316, obviously below the actual catch. Under the circumstances, complete totals can never be dependably attained.

It is interesting to note that states along the northern limit of the opossum's range report many opossum furs sold; perhaps the laws and regulations in these states are sufficiently specific and well enforced, so that the true number is approximated. The figures for each of these states are:

Minnesota	808	(1946)
Iowa	27,293	(1944)
Indiana	83,355	(1946)
Pennsylvania	110,850	(1944)
Wisconsin	7,859	(1945)
Illinois	121,202	(1947)
Ohio	119,485	(1944)
New York	3,852	(1948)

This is a goodly number for New York, since the opossum is a recent migrant into that state.

Of more than ordinary interest are the statistics on opossum pelts reported for Michigan. In his master's thesis (Michigan State College, 1942) Clarence C. Taube calls attention to the fact that no opossums were recorded for the counties in the southwestern corner of the state from about 1850 to near the end of the century, but they had been reported before 1850 and have since multiplied to an extraordinary extent, as the following figures on pelts sold within the state demonstrate:

1928–29	944	1932–33	6,864
1929–30	3,460	1933–34	11,290
1930–31	2,319	1934–35	26,042
1931–32	4,668	1938–39	18,634

Although the opossum was but recently introduced into the Pacific states, California reported 498 skins among the pelts sold, Oregon 107, and Washington 159.

Adding up the figures for the United States given in the Ashbrook report, we have a total annual catch for each year of the five-year period covered as follows:

1944	1,500,000	1947	1,100,000
1945	1,800,000	1948	1,100,000
1946	1,700,000		

The average for the years 1944 to 1948 is about 1,400,000 opossum skins sold into the fur market. If we select for each state the highest figure for any one year of the five-year period, the total comes to 2,300,000. Allowing for understatements in most items, it is more than likely that over 2,500,000 opossum skins find their way into the fur market each year. Parenthetically, the *Encyclopaedia Britannica*, fourteenth edition, states that 12,430,246 opossum skins were offered at auction, in 1927, in London. That the reader may have an idea of the extent of the total fur market in this country, the table below is adapted from the November, 1922, issue of the *Journal of Mammalogy*. It shows the number of furs used in the United States in the three-year period 1919–21.

Beaver, *Castor canadensis*	420,490
Muskrat, *Fiber zibethicus*	14,109,288
Nutria, *Myocastor coypu*	1,941,784
Squirrel, *Sciurus vulgaris*	14,858,316
White hare, *Lepus* sp	3,713,036
Mole, *Talpa* sp	23,801,908
Mink, *Putorius vison*	1,683,900
Weasel or ermine, *Putorius arcticus*	3,492,412
Kolinsky, *Mustela sibirica*	1,151,553
Skunk, *Mephitis* sp	6,895,674
Alaska fur seal, *Callorhinus alascanus*	85,164
Wolf, *Canis* sp	1,094,502
Red fox, *Vulpes fulvus*	1,295,258
Silver or black fox, *Vulpes fulvus*	26,350
Civet cat, *Spilogale* sp, *Viverra* sp	2,114,535
Raccoon, *Procyon* sp	1,713,700
Sea otter, *Latax lutris*	76
American opossum, *Didelphis virginiana*	9,787,742
Australian opossum, *Phalanger* sp	4,265,621
Ring-tailed opossum, *Pseudochirus* and *Phalanger*	1,321,625

Four female opossums (Didelphis virginiana) *two in the black phase and two in the gray phase. Photograph by J. M. Kuehne.*

Wombat (koala), *Phascolarctus*	
cinereus	208,677
Kangaroo, *Macropus* sp	41,238
Wallaby, *Macropus* sp	1,722,588
Total furs used	95,745,437

The data for high and low years, it may be seen from the Ashbrook report, do not synchronize for the various states, as would be expected if the supply were governed solely by world demand. Below are some examples of the numbers reported.

Florida	1,004	(1946)	8,339	(1947)
Georgia	3,594	(1945)	40,000	(1948)
Virginia	26,076	(1947)	45,349	(1948)
Texas	330,066	(1945)	91,461	(1948)

145

The tables presented in the Ashbrook report do, however, show an over-all downward trend in trapping activity in the last five years. The reason is not far to seek: it is due to a fall in the demand, and this trend seems likely to continue for some time, although eventual recovery of the market is also inevitable. A quotation on this point from "Wildlife Leaflet 315" (1950) of the Fish and Wildlife Service is instructive:

Warehouses are bulging with raccoon, opossum, skunk, fox and coyote furs. These are the "unwanted" furs, according to the trade designation. Many raw fur receiving companies have had to rent additional space to store the undesirable long-haired furs. A considerable number of raw furs are worth only 25 cents per pelt or less on the market and in some states local raw fur receiving houses are not buying certain species of long-haired furs. Nevertheless the industry has to hang on to the huge quantities of furs in the hope that a ready market will develop soon bringing better prices.

The market for "wanted" furs—muskrat, mink, squirrel, marmot and Persian lamb—remains good. Mink, both wild and raised, is the most profitable fur on the market at the present time. One and a half to two million mink were harvested by domestic ranchers alone last year. Importers of fur from Canada, Russia and other countries are still receiving furs. America has always consumed more furs than it produced and "dollar hungry" countries are still shipping in furs in hopes of a market.

Some of the ideas already advanced to build up the market for long-haired furs include shearing, clipping and dyeing to make "new and exotic" products. Already stylists have shown crimson and green fur coats. Experiments in the production of fancy leathers from unwanted furs also continues apace. Suede shoes, gloves, bill-folds and unique book-bindings are only a few of the products manufacturers hope to make out of such skins as raccoon, opossum and coyote.

This matter has been introduced here although it is more than likely that the picture will change before these lines are put into print. Yet the facts presented help to give some faint idea of the fur market in which the opossum is not a negligible competitor.

Such are the vicissitudes and uncertainties of a business that depends on the whims of style; but from the standpoint of conservation, a series of slack seasons should give the animal populations, especially the rarer and more desirable species, a chance to recoup their dwindling numbers. This is not good news for poultry raisers, especially the careless ones that go to little trouble to protect their flocks against nocturnal marauders.

The rough estimate of 2,500,000 opossums used annually for fur does not by any means cover the number of opossums killed. There must be added an indefinite number of hundreds of thousands which are used for food only and some tens of thousands that are caught by parties hunting for the fun of the chase. Many are killed and buried as vermin, and other thousands are crushed by automobiles on the highways.

All of these statistics pose problems in conservation. Already several important fur bearers are nearing extinction. The sea otter, first hunted by Russians on our western shores, has been saved only by timely government protection. The steady inroads into the opossum population have not yet had an appreciable effect on the industry, probably because of the unfailing fecundity of the species. Every important opossum state has established by law a closed season, which varies slightly with the latitude. The closed season lasts usually two months and includes the breeding season. The greater part of the year the pelt is worthless, and slaughter of the animal except for food is futile as well as unlawful.

Australia has long had the same problems of wanton destruction of wild game and has instituted measures of conservation similar to our own.

The rearing of opossums, except for scientific purposes, has no point. They are as expensive and troublesome to raise as mink or silver fox, and their pelts are of incomparably less value. The only opossum farms will continue to be university laboratories where the animals are raised for scientific investigation. Since they are born veritable embryos, they are particularly well adapted for many studies: sex development, hormone and drug action, development of the nervous system in relation to behavioral responses—in short, any investigation into how bodily functions arise. The opossum is "made to order" for such studies. Stupid as he is, he nevertheless makes a valuable contribution to the sum of human knowledge.

A possum feast in preparation, primitive style. Photograph by Underwood & Underwood.

148

22

Possum and Taters

Possum and taters—sweet taters, that is—these make a traditional dish in the South. It is customary to give your visitor from the North a possum dinner with all the trimmin's as an experience to talk about back home. When President Taft visited Georgia, he too feasted on possum, which event evoked an editorial in the June 26, 1909, number of *Harper's Weekly*. This editorial stressed the spirit of friendly co-operation engendered by possum hunts and the neighborhood dinners that follow them. The editorial goes on to point out that all Georgia governors who have amounted to anything have eaten possum and taters, except Allen C. Chandler, who "had a lean and hungry look anyway," wherein he differed greatly from rotund President Taft.

That a Northern governor can enjoy sampling possum roast is proved by the fact that our late President, Franklin D. Roosevelt, when he was governor of New York, not only participated in possum hunting in Georgia but also shared in the feast.

One possum roast, which began as a semi-private affair, expanded into an institution in which several counties participated. This was the Frankston, Texas, Possum Dinner. According to an account of the event in the *Dallas Sunday News* of December 4, 1938, the dinner was started by farmer W. W.

Scarbrough, owner of Scarbrough Springs, where the outings were held. G. C. Scarbrough of Houston, the founder's son, is authority for the statement that as many as eight thousand persons from the surrounding country assembled for the feast. The preparation for the dinner required the services of a dozen workers for a week. Not only was possum roast served but also venison, coon, elk, goat, duck, and turkey—all served picnic style to the accompaniment of brass bands or speeches by prominent Texans.

Traditionally opossum and sweet potatoes have been associated more particularly with the Southern Negro. Having lived in both central and eastern Texas, I can say that this holds less in the former than in the latter section of the state, possibly because of both the smaller proportion of Negroes in central Texas and the greater proportion of prairie to woodland in that section, with a scantier population of opossums. Working with hundreds of opossums at the University of Texas in the 1910's, I found no demand for opossum carcasses on the part of either whites or Negroes. Perhaps "University" opossums were under especial suspicion, which was probably well founded.

McAtee, writing on the mammals of Indiana, was certainly stretching a point when he bemoaned the fact that "because of the opossum's savory flesh few ever reach the museum." On this subject we have some statistics. In East Texas, where the Negro contingent of the population is quite concentrated, Professor Lay of the Texas Agricultural and Mechanical College made a poll of the consumption of opossums by Negroes. This he did by personally interviewing 2,098 boys at Civilian Conservation Corps camps at Lufkin and New Waverly. He found that 57.6 per cent of the interviewed boys of East Texas ate an average of 4.9 opossums a year; in round numbers, half of the boys indulged in opossum fare, and those who did consumed 5 opossums in a year. Broken down into city and country boys: 76 per cent of the latter did better than the city boys by three-fifths of an opossum per person. These statistics hardly argue for any special predilection for opossum meat in the region where this is cheap and readily procurable, especially during "hard times," times when CCC camps flourished under the New Deal.

The early explorers in America sampled opossum flesh, as would be expected, but they were by no means unanimous as to its edibility. John Lawson in his *History of Carolina* wrote: "I have of necessity in the wilderness eaten them. Their Flesh is very white and well tasted; but their ugly tailes put one out of conceit with that fare." But again, in another place he states: "The land we passed over this day was most of it good, and the worst passable. At night we killed a Possum, being cloy'd with Turkeys, made a dish of that, which tasted much better than young pork and veal, their Fat being as white as any I ever saw." Brickell, who purported to describe what he actually saw himself, nevertheless cribbed again from Lawson, writing in the same unenthusiastic vein: "Their flesh is generally fat, white and well tasted, several Persons eat of them, especially the *Indians* and *Negroes*, who prefer them before *Pork*, but their ugly tails are enough to put one out of conceipt of them."

The observant naturalist of the La Plata region, Rengger, was also quite content to leave the flesh of the opossum to the Indians. Perhaps he did not have in mind *Didelphis marsupialis*, but *Didelphis azarae*, the *micuré* or "stinker" in the local parlance, a species that would inspire gustatory caution. Similarly the East Indies, according to Valentyn, have their repulsive coescoes as well as palatable philander.

Some of the older as well as more modern writers on this subject mention the forbidding appearance of opossums in general. Du Tertre claimed that no one in the Antilles ate them. Alston contended that Costa Ricans do not consider the flesh good and that to him personally the whole appearance of the live animal was most uninviting. Gumilla reported that the natives of the Orinoco seek to destroy the opossum because of its depredations on banana, papaya, and other fruits, not for their flesh, "which tastes disgustingly."

From the very early book of adventure in America by Hans Stade, captive among the Amazon Indians from 1547 to 1555, come the first directions for the preparation of the opossum for cooking. It is desirable, he said, first to remove all excess fat from around the kidneys, which is the source of the fetid odor emitted by the animal. Stade concludes that, after this precaution is taken, the "flesh is tender and of the best quality." He was later much quoted on this point; De Léry lifted the passage from Stade verbatim, and the item is to be found in the *Dictionnaire raisonné* published a century later. Nearer our own time Dr. Barton wrote: "The opossum is now brought to the market in Philadelphia almost as regularly as the wild rabbit of the country, or as poultry." Fifty years later Audubon found opossums readily obtainable commercially.

From all this I would conclude that the Virginia opossum is not an offensive member of the Didelphidae; with this I am sure ten million opossum fans will agree.

150

Governor Franklin D. Roosevelt, of New York, helps himself to possum and taters at a dinner given in his honor at White Sulphur Springs, Georgia, by the Atlanta Association of Building Owners and Managers. Dr. Hope Tigner, of Atlanta, is at the left, and Miss Martha Tigner is serving Wide World Photos, Inc.

East Indian and Australian marsupials also have for ages constituted the chief source of animal food for the natives. Dampier sampled wallaby flesh, which he described as "a sort of raccoons . . . and like them . . . very good meat." The members of Captain James Cook's first expedition, landing in Eastern Australia, were glad to add fresh kangaroo and wallaby meat to their larder. One reads in Hawkesworth's account of the expedition:

July 14, 1770. The next day our kanguroo was dressed for dinner and proved most excellent meat.
July 27. On this day Mr. Gore shot a kanguroo,

which, with the skin, entrails, and head, weighed 84 pounds. Upon examination, however, we found that this animal was not at its full growth. We dressed it for dinner; but to our great disappointment we found it much worse flavour than we had eaten before.

Two years out from home and choosy about their food!

It seems to be characteristic of modern man that food must appeal to all of his senses as well as to his imagination. A dissonant note in this regard can ruin the appetite most readily. A mere name, for example, suggestive of the unclean, arouses a strong prejudice

151

against specific animals as food. Muskrat carcasses have to be sold on the market under the Indian name *musquash* or—just as euphoniously—as marsh rabbit. The suffix *-rat* is the offending portion of the usual name. Some years ago St. Louisans purchased "prairie squirrel" in their markets and relished the meat until they discovered that they were eating prairie dogs. Dogs, of all things! The prejudice hinged entirely on the name, for prairie dogs have no relation to the dog or any other carnivore; they are rodents and are kin to squirrels—only their bark somewhat resembles that of a small pup. Both prairie dogs and muskrats are strict herbivores and hence "clean," like rabbits.

A similar prejudice built up about a name is related by Mrs. Meredith concerning the otherwise quite palatable kangaroo rats of Tasmania: "Luckily for the poor little beasties," she writes, "no one fancies eating them because they are called *rats*; so that giving *them* an 'ill name' has been of great service to them." By the same token it might have been a good day for the opossum if "pouch rat," the English equivalent of the German *Beutelratte* or the Dutch *Boschrot,* or the French *rat de bois* had been attached to the species in America. As a "rat" many an opossum might have avoided the cooking pot.

The Southerner, smacking his lips for opossum, has his own idea of the palatability of the meat. Little does he care what explorers thought about it. But he does care about how his possum is prepared for the table. For several recipes presented here I am indebted to Mrs. F. V. B. Demarest, of Plainfield, New Jersey, who was born and reared in Nobelist William Faulkner's home town of Oxford, Mississippi.

Mississippi Possum and Taters

Scald the opossum with lye and scrape off hair. Dress whole, leaving on the head and the tail. Rub well with salt and put in a cool place over night. When ready to cook, settle in a deep pan with 1 quart of water, spread 3 or 4 slices of breakfast bacon across the breast, and put in oven. When half-done, remove from oven and stuff with a dressing made of bread crumbs, a small onion, salt and pepper, and opossum juice taken from the pan in which it has been cooking. Return to pan, place around it some small peeled sweet potatoes, and bake all until light brown, basting frequently with the gravy.

Possum and Taters, Mississippi Hillbilly Style

Skin opossum and remove insides; wash thoroughly in hot soda water, then rinse in cold water. When ready to cook, stick 12 cloves in a large onion; lay it inside opossum with a few bay leaves, after rubbing inside with 1 tablespoon salt and 1 tablespoon black pepper. Melt some fat in roasting pan and brown opossum all over. Put in oven, roasting and basting like any other meat. When nearly done, lay peeled sweet potatoes around it and cook until potatoes are brown and tender. Then eat, but don't forget to spare at least a few bones for those red hounds that helped you tree your possum.

Possum Stuffed with Chinquapins—Civil War Recipe

Skin the opossum, being sure to remove "musk" glands if the specimen is a male. Slit the carcass open, removing entrails; scald in boiling water, and scrape clean. Rub inside and out with salt and pepper and hang in a cool place.

When ready to cook the opossum, stuff it with equal parts boiled chinquapins (or chestnuts), applesauce, and bread crumbs. Sew up; surround with small peeled sweet potatoes and cover with 1 cup boiling water, ½ cup vinegar (or juice of 2 lemons), and daub with 1 tablespoon butter. Bake until tender and golden, basting often.

The sweet potatoes absorb a good deal of the fat, which improves their own flavor. If you prefer, remove excess fat from the opossum before dressing it.

Variation: Roast Possum with Sassafras

Clean opossum and rub with salt and pepper as above; but instead of stuffing, stick the outside full of fresh sassafras twigs until it bristles like a porcupine, and roast it, preferably on a spit before an open fire.

Tennessee Possum

Skin and clean the opossum and rub inside and outside with salt and pepper. Melt 3 tablespoons butter in a frying pan, and in it brown ½ onion, chopped fine, and the chopped liver of the opossum. When well browned, add ¾ cup bread crumbs, 1 teaspoon chopped parsley, salt, pepper, and enough beef broth to moisten. Stuff the body of the opossum with this mixture and sew up with a cotton string. Put in a baking pan with 2 tablespoons of water and roast in a hot oven, 450°, for 15 minutes. Lower the heat to 350° and continue cooking until meat is tender and a rich brown. Baste frequently with the following mixture: ½ cup water, 1 tablespoon butter, 1 teaspoon Worcestershire, salt, and pepper.

Serve hot.

Sweet Taters and Possum

First catch a young fat possum. This in itself affords excellent sport on moonlight nights in fall. Remove the fur either by skinning or by soaking the possum in hot lye water, being careful not to get any on the hands. Clean, take off the head and feet (unless you want to cook it like whole roast pig), and wash well. Salt the possum well inside and out and freeze overnight either outdoors or in the refrigerator compartment. When ready to cook, peel 8 sweet potatoes and boil them tender in slightly salted water to which 2 tablespoons of butter and 1 tablespoon of sugar have been added. At the same time, stew the possum tender in a tightly covered pan with a little water. Arrange the potatoes around the possum, strip with bacon, sprinkle with thyme or marjoram, or with pepper, and brown in the oven. Baste often with the drippings. Served hot, it sure is "a dish fo' a king."

ARTHUR and BOBBIE COLEMAN, *The Texas Cookbook* (New York, A. A. Wyn, Inc., 1949)

Alma's Recipe for Possum

Put ½ cup lime in about 1 gallon of boiling water and scald quickly and pull off hair while hot. Scrape well—remove feet, tail and entrails—like you would a pig. Cut off ears, remove eyes and head if desired. Pour hot water over it and clean thoroughly.

Put 1 cup salt in sufficient cold water to cover "possum," add 1 pod red pepper and let stand over night. In the morning remove salt water and pour boiling water over it. Cook in enough boiling water to boil up over "possum" but not enough to cover. Cook until skin can be pierced

with a fork easily, and let stand in water until ready for baking.

When ready to bake, place "possum" in pan with skin side up. Bake in a moderate oven until crisp and brown. If fire is too hot skin will blister and burn.

Carve "possum" and surround with potatoes (sliced or quartered) which have been previously baked.

MRS. S. R. DULL, *Southern Cooking* (New York, Grosset & Dunlap, 1941)

Possum and Taters

After the opossum is caught, place in pen and feed well for a week or two. Then kill and dress the opossum as you would a pig. Parboil in salt water with a pod or two of red pepper for seasoning. Remove from broth before it becomes tender. Place in baking dish and roast at 325° until tender but not too brown. Prepare sweet potatoes by boiling in the jackets until done but still firm. Remove skins, cut in quarters, and place around the opossum in the baking dish. If preferred, the sweet potatoes may be baked, then peeled, and placed around the opossum during the last 45 minutes–1 hour of roasting. When the opossum is very tender, well browned, and the potatoes are brown, remove to a hot platter and serve.

MISSISSIPPI EXTENSION SERVICE
State College, Mississippi

Although the opossum has migrated farther and farther north, recipes for possum and taters seem not to be keeping pace with him. At least directions for cooking opossum have not yet become an integral part of the more universally used cookbook. When an opossum recipe does appear in such a book, it sometimes starts with an apology such as: "Opossum is very fat with a peculiarly flavored meat." By that time one's zest for it is gone. It seems that the uninitiated Northerner must first develop a taste for the meat of this edible migrant. Not until *opossum* appears in the index of every cookbook will the North and South come to true gustatory understanding.

APPENDIX

Possum Rhymes and Folklore

IN HIS *Wild Animals of North America*, Edward W. Nelson, one-time chief of the United States Biological Survey, made the following comment: "The opossum lives in song and folklore of the South and has become the most widely known of American mammals."

The second part of this statement is open to question, but not the first, as the selections in this chapter will show.

The poetry of Paul Laurence Dunbar, the Homer of the opossum world, intrigued me half a century ago. His "Hunting Song" and "Possum" are reprinted by permission of Dodd, Mead and Company, Inc., from *The Complete Poems of Paul Laurence Dunbar*.

"Hunting Song" conjures up pictures which are both vivid and true.

HUNTING SONG

Tek a cool night, good an' cleah
  Skiff o' snow upon de groun';
Jes' 'bout fall-time o' de yeah
  W'en de leaves is dry an' brown;
Tek a dog an' tek a axe,
  Tek a lantu'n in yo' han',
Step light whah de switches cracks,
  Fu' dey's huntin' in de lan'.
Down thoo de valleys an' ovah de hills,
  Into de woods whah de 'simmon-tree grows,
Wakin' an' skeerin' de po' whippo' wills,

Huntin' fu' coon an' fu' 'possum we goes.
Blow dat ho'n dah loud an' strong,
  Call de dogs an' da'kies neah;
Mek its music cleah an' long,
  So de folks at home kin hyeah.
Blow it twell de hills an' trees
  Sen's de echoes tumblin' back;
Blow it twell de back'ard breeze
  Tells de folks we's on de track.
Coons is a-ramblin' an' 'possums is out;
  Look at dat dog; you could set on his tail!
Watch him now—steady,—min' what you's about,
  Bless me, dat animal's got on de trail!
Listen to him ba'kin' now!
  Dat means bus'ness, sho's you bo'n;
Ef he's struck de scent I 'low
  Dat ere 'possum's sholy gone.
Knowed dat dog fu' fo'teen yeahs,
  An' I nevah seed him fail
W'en he sot dem flappin' eahs
  An' went off upon a trail.
Run, Mistah 'Possum, an' run, Mistah Coon,
  No place is safe fu' yo' ramblin' to-night;
Mas' gin de lantu'n an' God gin de moon,
  An' a long hunt gins a good appetite.
Look hyeah, folks, you hyeah dat change?
  Dat ba'k is sha'per dan de res'.
Dat ere soun' ain't nothin' strange,—
  Dat dog's talked his level bes'.
Somep'n' 's treed, I know de soun'.
  Dah now,—wha'd I tell you? see!
Dat ere dog done run him down;
  Come hyeah, he'p cut down dis tree.
Ah, Mistah 'Possum, we got you at las'—
  Needn't play daid, laying dah on de groun';
Fros' an' de 'simmons has made you grow fas',—
  Won't he be fine when he's roasted up brown!

154

The sentiments towards opossum roast in "Possum" are still nostalgic to many a former resident of the South.

POSSUM

Ef dey's anyt'ing dat riles me
    An' jes' gits me out o' hitch,
Twell I want to tek my coat off,
    So's to r'ar an' t'ar an' pitch,
Hit's to see some ign'ant white man
    'Mittin' dat owdacious sin—
W'en he want to cook a possum
    Tekin' off de possum's skin.
W'y dey ain't no use in talkin',
    Hit jes' hu'ts me to de hea't
Fu' to see dem foolish people
    Th'owin' 'way de fines' pa't.
W'y, dat skin is jes' es tendah
    An' ez juicy ez kin be;
I knows all erbout de critter—
    Hide an' haih—don't talk to me!
Possum skin is jes lak shoat skin;
    Jes' you swinge an' scrope it down,
Tek a good sha'p knife an' sco' it,
    Den you bake it good an' brown.
Huh-uh! honey, you's so happy
    Dat yo' thoughts is 'mos' a sin
When you's seetin' dah a-chawin'
    On dat possum's cracklin' skin.
White folks t'ink dey know 'bout eatin',
    An' I reckon dat dey do
Sometimes git a little idee
    Of a middlin' dish er two:
But deh ain't a t'ing dey knows of
    Dat I reckon cain't be beat
W'en we set down at de table
    To a unskun possum's meat!

The minor rhymes included are only samples of the many which are floating about in the rural districts of the South.

POSSUM HUNTING

"Oh, git away little chillun,
Doan yo bodder me,
I'se sweet as 'lasses candy
Dat's as sweet as sweet can be.
    "Oh, git away little chillun,
Doan yo bodder me,
If I climbs a tree a-tall
It'll be a possum tree."

Southern Folk Song

AN OPOSSUM HUNT

'Possum meat is good an' sweet,
I always finds it good to eat.
My dog tree, I went to see.
A great big 'possum up dat tree.
I retch up an' pull him in,
Den dat ole 'possum 'gin to grin.
I tuck him home an' dressed him off.
Dat night I laid him in de fros'.
De way I cooked dat 'possum sound,
I fust parboiled, den baked him brown.
I put sweet taters in de pan.
'Twus de bigges' eatin' in de lan'.
        THOMAS W. TALLEY, *Negro Folk Rhymes*
        (New York, Macmillan, 1922)

RACCOON AND OPOSSUM FIGHT

De raccoon an' de 'possum
Under de hill a-fightin';
Rabbit almos' bust his sides
Laughin' at de bitin'.
De raccoon claw de 'possum
Along de ribs an' head;
'Possum tumble over an' grin,
Playin' lak he been dead.
        THOMAS W. TALLEY, *Negro Folk Rhymes*

COON AND 'POSSUM

Coon saw a 'possum
Runnin' on his ground.
Said "Look out Br'er 'Possum,
Don't mash my 'taters down."
    Chorus
Down, down, down, low down,
Put 'em in to bake 'em,
Pull 'em out to brown.
        Furnished by J. L. Pierce

SHAKE THE PERSIMMONS DOWN

De raccoon up in de 'simmon tree,
Dat 'possum on de groun',
De 'possum say to de raccoon:
            "Suh!"
"Please shake dem 'simmons down."
De raccoon say to de 'possum: "Suh!"
(As he grin from down below),
"If you wants dese good 'simmons, man,
Jes clam up whar dey grow."
        THOMAS W. TALLEY, *Negro Folk Rhymes*

"De Fust Banjo" has been a source of amusement for years—and by the way, the reference to the tendons of the opossum's tail as a source of banjo strings calls to mind the use of the kangaroo tail tendons as a source of a certain kind of surgical suture.

DE FUST BANJO

Go 'way, fiddle! folks is tired o' hearin' you a-squawkin'.
Keep silence fur yo' betters!—don't you heah de banjo talkin'?
About de possum's tail she's gwine to lecter—ladies, listen!—
About de ha'r whut isn't dar, an' why de ha'r is missin':
"Dar's gwine to be a' oberflow," said Noah, lookin' solemn—
Fur Noah tuk de "Herald," an' he read de ribber column—
An' so he sot his hands to wuk a-cl'arin' timber-patches,
An' 'lowed he's gwine to build a boat to beat the steamah *Natchez*.
Ol' Noah kep' a-nailin' an' a-chippin' an' a-sawin';
An' all de wicked neighbors kep' a-laughin' an' a-pshawin';
But Noah didn't min' 'em, knowin' whut wuz gwine to happen:
An' forty days an' forty nights de rain it kep' a-drappin.
Now, Noah had done cotched a lot ob ebry sort o' beas'es—
Ob all de shows a-trabbelin', it beat 'em all to pieces!
He had a Morgan colt an' sebral head o' Jarsey cattle—
An' druv 'em 'board de Ark as soon's he heered de thunder rattle.
Den sech anoder fall ob rain!—it come so awful hebby,
De ribber riz immejitly, an' busted troo de lebbee;
De people all wuz drownded out—'cep' Noah an' de critters,
An' men he'd hired to work de boat—an' one to mix de bitters.
De Ark she kep' a-sailin' an' a-sailin' *an'* a-sailin';
De lion got his dander up, an' like to bruk de palin';
De sarpints hissed; de painters yelled; tell, whut wid all de fussin',
You c'u'dn't hardly heah de mate a-bossin' 'roun' an' cussin'.

Now Ham, de only nigger whut wuz runnin' on de packet,
Got lonesome in de barber-shop, an' c'u'dn't stan' de racket;
An' so, fur to amuse he-se'f, he steamed some wood an' bent it,
An' soon he had a banjo made—de fust dat wuz invented.
He wet de ledder, stretched it on; made bridge an' screws an' aprin;
An' fitted in a proper neck—'twuz berry long an' tap'rin';
He tuk some tin, an' twisted him a thinble fur to ring it;
An' den de mighty question riz: how wuz he gwine to string it?
De 'possum had as fine a tail as dis dat I's a-singin';
De ha'r's so long an' thick an' strong,—des fit fur banjo-stringin';
Dat nigger shaved 'em off as short as wash-day-dinner graces;
An' sorted ob 'em by de size, f'om little E's to basses.
He strung her, tuned her, struck a jig,—'twuz "Nebber min' de wedder,"—
She soun' like forty-lebben bands a-playin' all togedder;
Some went to pattin'; some to dancin': Noah called de figgers;
An' Ham he sot an' knocked de tune, de happiest ob niggers!
Now, sence dat time—it's mighty strange—dere's not de slightes' showin'
Ob any ha'r at all upon de 'possum's tail a-growin';
An' curi's, too, dat nigger's ways; his people nebber los' 'em—
Fur whar you finds de nigger—dar's de banjo an' de 'possum!

IRWIN RUSSELL (1853–79)

The next two poems are from John Charles McNeill's *Lyrics from Cotton Land* and are used with the permission of the University of North Carolina Press.

THE TRICKSTER TRICKED

Long ways fum home I wus huntin' my cow.
  She's done en los' her bell,
En which-a-way she wus travelin', how
  Does you reckin I could tell?
Hongry en hot, weak en tar'd,
  I wus 'bout to turn aroun',

156

Dominican opossum grinning even while playing possum. Photograph by Paul Griswald Howes.

When I seed ol' Rattler grabblin' hard
  Atter supp'n' in de groun'.
I breaks a switch en twis' it 'bout
  Down dar, en den I pull
Till my holt break, en dat switch bring out
  A passle er 'possum wool!
'T wa'n't many minutes, bless yo' life,
  'Fo' I felt lak anudder man:
I was gwine on home to see my wife
  Wid a 'possum in my han'!
Knowin' his ways, I hilt him so
  He couldn' ketch my pants.
He'd not take long to do his do
  'F I gin him half a chance.
'Twus up hill den, en down hill now,
  Lak a man wut's bein' paid—
When all er sudden I seed my cow
  Asleep in a dog'ood shade!
"Whoo-hee!" I hollered: up she flounce
  En her runnin' was enough.
Right den I, too, wus on de bounce
  To head dat heifer off.
Fergittin' wut wus in my han',
  I flop him 'g'inst my shin.
It didn' take long to change my plan

When I felt dem teef sink in.
At fust I tried to snatch him loose,
  But one jerk made me quit;
Dat varmint had to have some scuse
  Befo' he gwine a spit.
I laid down, lak I 'us fallin' sleep,
  Workin' de 'possum trick,
But smiles wus powerful hard to keep,
  'Ca'se it hurt lak a thousan' brick!
When he felt his tail done been sot free,
  He thought 'twus time to go.
I reck'n he jedged he 'us foolin' me,
  'Ca'se he open' his mouf right slow.
He started off—but we wa'n't gone fur
  'Fo' Rattler counted in,
En 'doubt no cradle or nairy a song,
  Putt him to sleep ag'in.
I let dat cow go on her way,
  Runnin' herse'f a race.
You kin drive yo' cow home any day,
  But a 'possum's meat is sca'ce.
Oh, I sucked his bones en sopped his juice.
  Thinks I, "Now wa'n't dat slick!
Dis possum I's et didn' have no scuse
  To be beat at his own ol' trick."

'POSSUM TIME AGAIN

Oh, dip some 'taters down in grease
En fling de dogs a 'tater apiece.
Ram yo' brogans clean er tacks,
Split de splinters en fetch de ax.
    It's 'possum time again!

Catfish tender, catfish tough,
We's done et catfish long enough.
We's tar'd er collards en white side-meat,
En we's gwine have supp'n' wut's good to eat.
    It's 'possum time again!

De pot's gwine simmer en blubber en bile
Till it gits scummed over wid 'possum ile.
But le's don't brag till we gits de goods.
Whoop! Come along, boys! We's off to de woods.
    It's 'possum time again!

From the wealth of opossum folklore, I have selected a short series of stories, which are reprinted here with grateful acknowledgment to the authors and publishers. Since these stories are more or less typical, I trust that they will afford the reader a good idea of this phase of our subject.

THE STORY OF OPOSSUM

(Featuring the pouch, first version)

Opossum lived with her children. Big Bat got them and carried them off to a hole in the rocks. Then Opossum went about crying. Presently Wolf came to her and said, "Why are you crying?" "Oh, I am crying because something big has stolen my children and taken them into a hollow in the rocks." Then Wolf said, "Guide me to the place." So she guided him to the place and he disappeared inside. Scarcely had he gotten in, however, when he began to curse, and was so scared that he ran back and came out. "I can't do it," he said, and he disappeared.

Opossum kept on crying continually until Rabbit came and said to her, "Why are you crying?" "Oh, I am crying because something big has taken my children from me and hidden them in a hole in the rocks." "Where is the place?" he said. "Go and show it to me." She guided him thither and pointed it out. Then he went inside. But scarcely had he gotten started when he cursed and was so scared that he ran back out. "I can't do anything," he said, and he went off.

Now while she was walking about crying continually, Highland-terrapin came up. He said, "Why are you crying?" "I am crying because something big has taken away my children and carried them off to a hole in the rocks." Then Terrapin said, "Show me the place." She guided him to it and said, "Here it is." Then he went inside. When he had nearly reached the young opossums he stepped on some hot ashes and cried out "Wim+ká p'aihehehó." But he went straight on, grasped the little opossums, and started out with them. He came along with them and got them out. Then the bat flew out and disappeared.

When Highland-terrapin got back he cut Opossum open under her navel and said to her, "Keep them here. Before they have stopped nursing, let them go." And he said to her, "They have stopped."

JOHN R. SWANTON, *Myths and Tales of the Southeastern Indians, Bulletin 88,* Bureau of American Ethnology, Smithsonian Institution, 1929

THE STORY OF OPOSSUM

(Featuring the pouch, second version)

Tcukbilabila (a brownish woodbird) carried off Opossum's children and kept them in a hole. Tcukbilabila sat upon them. Opossum went to the place and asked for them, but he would not give them to her. Opossum stayed there begging for them but could not get them. Then Terrapin went in to help her, upon which Tcukbilabila sang, "Sparks of hot ashes," and struck sparks. Then Terrapin went back. By and by Terrapin said that although he would not give him Opossum's children he would go and get them, and bring them back and put them into Opossum's belly. Terrapin did so, and he tied Opossum's children to her hips where she has carried them ever since.

JOHN R. SWANTON, *Myths and Tales*

WHY THE OPOSSUM HAS NO HAIR ON HIS TAIL

(Astute observation on opossum reproduction)

When there was a great flood all the animals were put in the ark, except the male opossum. A female opossum climbed up on the side of the ark and when the waters rose, her tail hung down into the water. When the waters subsided

158

it was found that all the hair on her tail had come off and ever since then the opossum's tail has been without hair.

All of the male opossums were drowned, so this female went off alone feeling ashamed, and coiled herself up as if dead. Her nose was near her side, and after breathing a long time in this position little opossums appeared in her pouch, and thus the young opossums have been born ever since.

JOHN R. SWANTON, *Myths and Tales*

WHY THE 'POSSUM'S TAIL IS BARE

(Playing possum and grinning)

'Possum used to have a long, bushy tail and he was so proud of it that he combed it out every morning and sang about it at the dance. Now Rabbit had had no tail since Bear pulled it off because he was jealous. Therefore he planned to play a trick on 'Possum.

The animals called a great council. They planned to have a dance. It was Rabbit's business to send out the news. One day as he was passing 'Possum's house, he stopped to talk.

"Are you going to the council?" he asked.

"Yes, if I can have a special seat," said 'Possum. "I have such a handsome tail I ought to sit where everyone can see me."

Rabbit said, "I will see that you have a special seat. And I will send someone to comb your tail for the dance." 'Possum was very much pleased.

Rabbit at once went to Cricket, who is an expert hair cutter; therefore the Indians call him the barber. He told Cricket to go the next morning and comb 'Possum's tail for the dance. He told Cricket just what to do.

In the morning, Cricket went to 'Possum's house. 'Possum stretched himself out on the floor and went to sleep, while Cricket combed out his tail and wrapped a red string around it to keep it smooth until night. But all the time, as he wound the string around, he was snipping off the hair closely. 'Possum went to the council and took his special seat. When it was his turn to dance, he loosened the red string from his tail and stepped into the middle of the lodge.

The drummers began to beat the drum. 'Possum danced around the circle again, singing, "See what a fine color it has." They all shouted again . . . . 'Possum wondered what it meant. He looked around. Every man was laughing at him. Then he looked down at his beautiful tail. It was bare as a lizard's tail. There was not a hair on it.

He was so astonished and ashamed that he could not say a word. He rolled over on the ground and grinned, just as he does today when taken by surprise.

KATHARINE B. JUDSON, Cherokee story from *Myths and Legends of the Mississippi Valley and the Great Lakes* (Chicago, A. C. McClurg and Company, 1914)

WHY THE OPOSSUM HAS NO HAIR ON HIS TAIL

The Raccoon met the Opossum, and the Opossum said: "How did you make such pretty rings on your tail?"

The Raccoon replied: "I wrapped bark around my tail and stuck it into the fire."

Then the Opossum got some bark, wrapped it around his tail, which then had hair on it, and built a fire. He stuck his tail into the fire and burned all of the hair off and ever since then opossums have had no hair on their tails.

JOHN R. SWANTON, *Myths and Tales*
(Tuggle Collection)

OPOSSUM AND SKUNK

(Opossum's grin and drool)

Opossum used to have a bushy tail. Skunk's tail was slender and bare, and Opossum saw it and laughed at him. Traveling along behind him he said, "Skunk's tail is lofga ('scraped'); my tail is watalwatal" (Opossum language). Then Skunk became angry, but he did not know what he could do about it. After they had traveled a considerable time he said, "I wish I could clip your tail." So he hunted up his friend Cricket, and talked to him. "Opossum called me 'Lofga tail.' When he is asleep go to him, cut his tail off, and fix it on my tail. Then, when Opossum gets up we will laugh at him." He did so. Since then Opossum has been so sad that he always keeps his mouth open and drools.

JOHN R. SWANTON, *Myths and Tales*

WHY THE OPOSSUM LOOKS ASHAMED

One time an Opossum got very hungry. He went about the world hunting something to eat. At last he looked up into a tree and saw some big balls hanging low down on the limbs. They looked so fine that he danced around the tree for joy.

After his dance he jumped up and caught one of the balls and mashed it in his mouth. It was very bitter, for it was an oak ball. He felt so bad that he crawled away, lay down, and made out that he was dead. Whenever anyone comes where he is, he remembers his mistake and feels ashamed of having been so badly deceived.

JOHN R. SWANTON, *Myths and Tales*

WHY 'POSSUM HAS A LARGE MOUTH

Very little food there was for Deer one dry season. He became thin and weak. One day he met 'Possum. Deer at once exclaimed, "Why, 'Possum, how fat you are! How do you keep so fat when I cannot find enough to eat?"

'Possum said, "I live on persimmons. They are very large this year, so I have all I want to eat."

"How do you get the persimmons?" asked Deer. "They grow so high!"

"That is easy," said 'Possum. "I go to the top of a high hill. Then I run down and strike a persimmon tree so hard with my head that all the ripe persimmons drop on the ground. Then I sit there and eat them."

"That is easily done," said Deer. "I will try it. Now watch me."

'Possum waited. Deer went to the top of a nearby hill. He ran down and struck the tree with his head. 'Possum watched him, laughing. He opened his mouth so wide while he laughed that he stretched it. That is why 'Possum has such a large mouth.

KATHARINE B. JUDSON, *Myths and Legends*

PLAYING DEAD TWICE IN THE ROAD

Once a rabbit and wolf went out one day to catch some fish. The wolf caught all the fish, and the rabbit didn't catch any. So the rabbit said to himself, "I am going home to my wife." Then he said to the wolf, "Brer Wolf, you have caught all the fish, and I have not caught any; and to-morrow morning your wife will be eating fish, and mine will be qu'rrling."—"I don't care," said Brer Wolf. "Please give me some fish for my wife!"—"I'll not, Brer Rabbit." Then Brer Rabbit said to himself, "Never mind! I will go and lie in the road where Brer Wolf has got to come along." Brer Rabbit went and laid in the middle of the road. The wolf came along with his basket of fish. The old rabbit pretended to be dead. Brer Wolf kicked him over, and said, "Ha! here is an old dead rabbit," and passed on. The rabbit went under the hill and got in the road again, and lay in the road as if he was dead. The old wolf came on and kicked him over, and said,

"Ha! here is another dead rabbit," and passed on. Brer Rabbit went around him and got into the road again. When Brer Wolf came along to this dead rabbit, he set his basket of fish down, and went back to get the first rabbit; and then the rabbit got his basket of fish.

A. M. BACON and E. C. PARSONS, "Folk-Lore from Elizabeth City County, Virginia," *Journal of American Folk-Lore*, 1922

A STORY ABOUT 'POSSUM
(Playing possum)

Once upon a time, Mr. 'Possum was out hunting something to eat. He saw a farmer coming home from town. He pretended to be dead right in the road. So the farmer jumped out and threw him into the wagon, and went on. The 'Possum threw the meat out of the wagon, got out himself and trotted off with it. He commenced to eat it, when Mr. Wolf came along, and asked him where and how he got it. The 'Possum told his story to the wolf. Said the Wolf, "Well, my friend, I must try it. I am very hungry." Sure enough, a farmer was coming, so he "played dead" in the middle of the road. When the farmer came and got out of the wagon, he got his axe and chopped the Wolf's head off. The Wolf thought he was going to put him into the wagon like the 'Possum, but he "got left," and an end was put to his life.

MARY LASLEY, "Sac and Fox Tales," *Journal of American Folk-Lore*, 1902

One short tale must suffice from Charles C. Jones, Jr.'s collection of *Negro Myths from the Georgia Coast* (Houghton Mifflin Company, 1888), done in the delightful vernacular of a unique class of colored folk residing in an isolated district.

BUH ROCCOON AN BUH POSSUM

Buh Roccoon ax Buh Possum wuh mek, wen de dog tackle um, eh double up ehself, an kibber eh yeye wid eh han, an wunt fight lucker man an lick de dog off. Buh Possum grin eh teet same lucker fool, an eh say, wen de dog come pon topper um, dem tickle him rib so bad long dem mout dat him bleege ter laugh; an so him furgit fuh fight.

Coward man hab all kind er lie fuh tell fuh scuse ehself.

Versions of this tale had a wide circulation. From Elsie Clews Parsons' *Tales from Guilford County, North Carolina,* for example we have this:

TICKLING 'POSSUM

Coon tell 'Possum, "Why you didn't fight?" Ole 'Possum said: "Dog tickle him so he couldn't fight fur laughin'."

Now follows an opossum story in the vernacular of the Louisiana bayous. It is reprinted from Harnett T. Kane's *Deep Delta Country* (New York, Duell, Sloan and Pearce, 1944).

PLAYING POSSUM

I trap' all day. When I get back to camp, I am blow' out an' hongry. At the camp I ax my wife what he have cook. "Not much, vieux," he say. "I pick up a few swimp an' crab. With these, I have make a gombo." "A gombo, chère, is very lil' for a man fatigue' like me. For what you don' kill a chicken?" My wife say "We have only one lef' an' he lay egg every day. It would be mortal sin to kill a beas' like that."

At the same secon' I hear "qua-ak! qua-ak!" I run, throw open the door, an' what I see? A big rat-de-bois have grab our las' hen by the neck. "Yas, ahn?" I holler, an' give him a coup de baton what put his feet in the air. "Look," I tell my wife, "le Bon Dieu est bon, oui. I will skin the possum. Zebe in the nex' camp, he will give me bottle wine for the hide. You will cook the meat. With gombo, wine an' it, an' bread and café, we will eat good." My wife find two-three potato, an' everything come good.

Befo' we start to eat, with the wine ope' on the table an' that gombo in the bowl, she ope' the do' of the stove to look how ev'ything is go. Maybe you not believe it, but there was the rat-de-bois stand up in that pan! He have eat the potato an' drink the grease. Now he jomp out the stove, he pass between my wife leg, an' on the table. He turn over the gombo, knock over the wine, then he run out the back door, me behin' 'im. Outside was the poor hen still on the groun', his neck all twis', his eye making comme-ci, comme-ça. That rat grab him as he pass an' run away in the grass. That was not all, no. That night he go to Zebe' camp an' take his skin from the stretching board an' put it back on. Now that was something, ahn?

After a drawing in Nature Magazine, *May, 1927.*

In their folklore the Mayans, too, gave their imagination free rein and personified the animals of their environment, as is illustrated by the following story which has come to me from the late Morris Steggerda, who had spent much time studying the present Mayan peoples. The story was written out for me in Mayan with the English rendition in parallel columns by Pedro Costello, a schoolteacher in Dzitas, Yucatán. The story is seen to have a relatively modern slant, since there were no chickens in Mexico until the Spaniards brought them in after the Conquest.

A MAYAN STORY

There was a poor hunter, who, having lost his way in the woods, saw a very large snake pinned down by a large stone. The man pitied the serpent and released him by taking up the stone and letting him loose and free to go, but the snake threatened to swallow the man, who said: "Look here, why are you trying to get me when I have just worked a good deed for you?" And the snake answered, "Who told you to let me loose?"

At that moment a leopard passed by, and the man stopped him and said, "Look here, is it justice that this snake should eat me up, because I freed him from a stone that pressed him and held him prisoner?" And the leopard answered, "It is good that he should swallow you up," and started running. Then a tiger passed by, and the man asked him: "Listen, is it justice that this snake should swallow me up when I have done him a good act?" And the tiger answered, "It is doing you justice," and he also ran away.

Then an opossum arrived and the man asked him: "Little opossum, is it good that this snake should swallow me up when I have taken away a large stone that pressed his back and was killing him?" And the opossum answered: "Tell this snake to coil himself up where he was formerly and then I will sentence rightly"; and he told the man, "When the snake coils up, place the stone on him as before." So the man did this and the snake was pinioned down again. And the opossum told the man: "Now shoot the snake dead." And the man did so. Then he addressed the man: "Now listen, I ask you two favors for the good deed I did for you. The first one is that you should bury all the opossums you find dead, and you find lying in your path, please bury them." "All right," said the man, "but I have lost my way home." And the opossum said, "I will show you your way home"; and the opossum showed the man his way.

Walking down the road he saw a dead opossum and buried it. After a while he saw another opossum and he took it up and buried it and then another. He buried it also. In this way he went on seeing dead opossums and burying them, but at last he saw another opossum lying dead. Being tired of his job, he lifted this one by the tail and was about to strike it hard upon the ground when the opossum came to and, making a loud noise, protesting against this action, said to him: "Is that the way you repay the good service I have done unto you when I rescued you from the fangs of the serpent?" The man feeling ashamed said: "I beg your pardon, little opossum, I didn't know it was you." And then the opossum answered: "Listen, then, to what I am going to tell you. I forgive you on one condition and that is my second plea to you: you must allow me to get into your yard in which you keep your chicken coop. And not only me, but also my children and relatives, you must allow us all to get into the chicken coop to feed ourselves." "All right then," said the man, "you may come."

When the man reached his home he told his wife about his troubles, but he did not tell her about the second agreement with the opossum. When night came a great noise was heard among the chickens. They were being eaten by the opossums. The wife awoke and said to the man: "The opossum is eating our chickens." They rushed out, cutlass in hand, and then called their dogs and began to kill all the opossums they found in their chicken coop.

Thus ended the life of the little opossum.

Note that these stories are for the most part of an explanatory sort; they are attempts to account for natural phenomena. Each story quoted revolves around some outstanding characteristic of the opossum. T. T. Waterman (1914) has called attention to this quality in the folk stories of the American Indian and of the native Southerner in these words:

Some tales exist, the plot of which would almost imply that a certain explanation was had in view when the plot was devised. I should like to give an example or two of this. The Fox Indians recount the story which deals with an encounter between an opossum and a skunk. Skunk, who is very sly, convinces opossum that his tail is a snake. As he springs away in alarm, his tail, of course, follows him. He dashes away so fast in trying to escape, that all the fur is worn off his tail by friction with the ground. The conclusion of the story is: "That is why the opossum has such a wretched, hairless tail." One has to admit that the Indian myth-maker had noted that the opossum's naked tail is conspicuously different from that of other animals, and set to work to explain it, for the tale fits the facts so nicely.

It is true, as Waterman says, that the opossum stories do nicely fit the facts of opossum behavior, but they do more—they reflect human behavior, emotions, and desires as well.

162

Bibliography

Aldrovandi, Ulisse (1522–1605). *De quadrupedibus.* Bononi, 1637.

Ash, Thomas (fl. 1682). *Carolina: or, A Description of the Present State of That Country.* 1682.* Reprinted in *Magazine of History,* Extra No. 59, 1917. See also Alexander S. Salley.

Ashton, John (b. 1834). *Curious Creatures in Zoology.* London, J. C. Nimmo, 1890.

Audubon, John James (1780–1851), and John Bachman (1790–1874). *The Quadrupeds of North America.* New York, V. G. Audubon, 1851–54. 3 vols.

Bachman, John (1790–1874). "Notes on the Generation of the Virginia Opossum, *Didelphys virginiana.*" Philadelphia Academy of Natural Sciences, *Proceedings,* Vol. IV (1848), 40–47.

———. "Remarks on Michel's Paper on the Generation of *Didelphys virginiana.*" American Association for the Advancement of Science, *Proceedings,* Vol. IV (1851), 60–67.

Banks, Sir Joseph (1743–1820). *Journal of the Right Hon. Sir Joseph Banks . . . during Captain Cook's First Voyage in H. M. S. Endeavour in 1768-71 to Terra del Fuego, Otahite, New Zealand, Australia, the Dutch East Indies, etc.* Edited by Sir Joseph D. Hooker. London, Macmillan and Company, Ltd., 1896.

NOTE: Asterisks indicate the editions consulted when more than one edition is mentioned.

Barber, Edwin A. (1851–1916). "Mound Pipes," *American Naturalist,* Vol. XVI, No. 4 (April, 1882), 265–81.

Barbour, Thomas. *Reptiles and Amphibians: Their Habits and Adaptations.* Boston, Houghton Mifflin Company, 1934.

Barton, Benjamin Smith (1766–1815). *Facts, Observations, and Conjectures Relative to the Generation of the Opossum of North-America. In a Letter . . . to Mons. Roume, of Paris.* Philadelphia, printed by Thomas and George Palmer, 1806.

———. *Additional Facts, Observations, and Conjectures Relative to the Generation of the Opossum of North-America. In a Letter to Professor J. A. H. Reimarus, of Hamburg.* Philadelphia, printed by S. Merritt, 1813. This and the preceding paper are in the Library of the University of Pennsylvania.

Benzoni, Girolamo (1519–1570?). *Beschryvinghe van West-Indien.* No. 18 of G. J. Saeghman's *Collection of Voyages.* Amsterdam, 1664.

Berlandier, Luis, and Rafael Chovel. *Diario de viage de la Comisión de Límites.* Mexico, Tipografía de Juan R. Navarro, 1850. The Comisión visited Texas.

Bewick, Thomas (1753–1828). *A General History of Quadrupeds.* First edition, 1790. First American edition by A. Anderson, New York, printed by G. and R. Waite, 1804. Bewick revived the art of woodcut engraving.

Bingley, William (1774–1823). *Animal Biography: or, Authentic Anecdotes of the Lives, Manners, and Economy of the Animal Creation, Arranged according to the System of Linnaeus.* Third edition. Vol. I, *Quadrupeds.* London, printed for R. Phillips, 1805.

[Boreman, Thomas], probable author. *A Description of Some Curious and Uncommon Creatures . . . for the Entertainment of Young People.* London, 1739. Copper plates.

Brickell, John (1710?–45). *The Natural History of North-Carolina.* Dublin, 1737. Reprinted by J. Bryan Grimes, by authority of the North Carolina Public Libraries, 1911.*

Bruyn, Cornelis de (1652–1726?). *Travels into Muscovy, Persia, and Parts of the East-Indies.* 1737.* Dutch edition, 1698; French, 1711. Contains 320 copper plates from the author's paintings; first illustration of any marsupial outside America.

Bry, Theodor de (1528–98), and his sons Johann Israel and Johann Theodor. *Collectiones peregrinationum in Indiam Orientalem et Indiam Occidentalem.* Frankfurt am Main, 1590–1634. Complete collection in the Peabody Library, Baltimore. The De Brys were copper-engravers, whose now rare books of travel were world famous. The opossum was featured in three De Bry volumes. The father also illustrated Harriot's work on the natural history of Virginia. Johann Theodor's son-in-law, Matthew Merian, furnished the engravings for Johnston's *De quadrupedibus* (the English Gesner) in 1657; and Merian's daughter, Maria, painted *Didelphis dorsigera,* from which the copper engraving was made for her *Insects of Surinam* (Amsterdam, 1717).

Buckland, Francis T., or Frank (1826–80). *Curiosities of Natural History.* First edition. London, 1857.* Reprinted by The Macmillan Company, New York, 1900.

Buffon, Georges Louis Leclerc, Comte de (1707–88). *L'Histoire naturelle, générale et particulière.* Vols. IV–XV of the first edition (Paris, 1749*), written with the aid of Louis Jean Marie Daubenton (1716–1800), constitute the famous *History of Quadrupeds* and contain unsurpassed steel engravings of animals.

Byrd, William (1674–1744). *Natural History of Virginia, or the Newly Discovered Eden.* Edited and translated from the German version (1737) by R. C. Beatty and William J. Mulloy. Richmond, Dietz Press, 1940.

Byrne, Muriel St. Clare. *The Elizabethan Zoo: A Book of Beasts, both Fabulous and Authentic.* London, F. Etchells and H. MacDonald, 1926. Selections from Topsell, Pliny, and others.

Cabrera, Ángel, and José Yepes. *Historia natural Ediar: Mamíferos sud-americanos.* Illustrated by Carlos C. Wiedner. Buenos Aires, Compañía Argentina de Editores, 1940.

Catesby, Mark (1679?–1749). *The Natural History of Carolina, Florida and the Bahama Islands.* London, 1731–43. Revised by Mr. Edwards, 1754.*

Coupin, H. E. V., and John Lea. *The Romance of Animal Arts and Crafts.* London, Seeley, Service and Company, Ltd., 1907.

Cowper, William (1666–1709). "Account of the Anatomy of Those Parts of the Male Opossum That Differ from the Female." Royal Philosophical Society, *Transactions,* Vol. XIV (1704).

Cuvier, Georges Léopold Frédéric Dagobert, Baron (1769–1832). *Le règne animal.* Paris, 1817. Second edition, 1829–30.* English edition by Edward Griffith: *The Animal Kingdom.* London, 1827–32. *The Class* Mammalia. London, 1827.*

Davis, David E. "The Home Range of Some Brazilian Mammals," *Journal of Mammalogy,* Vol. XXVI, No. 2 (May, 1945), 119–27.

Dearborn, Ned. *Foods of Some Predatory Fur-bearing Animals in Michigan. Bulletin No. 1,* University of Michigan, School of Forestry and Conservation. Ann Arbor, University of Michigan Press, 1932.

Del Campo, Rafael Martín. "Ensayo de interpretación del libro undécimo de la *Historia general de las cosas de Nueva España,* de Fray Bernardino de Sahagún.—III. *Los mamíferos.*" Instituto de Biología, *Anales,* Vol. XII (1941), 489–506.

Dictionnaire raisonné et universel des animaux ou le règne animal. Vol. III. Paris, 1759. Oliver Goldsmith owned a copy.

Dobie, J. Frank. *The Voice of the Coyote.* Boston, Little, Brown and Company, 1949.

Dumont de Montigny, Lieutenant. *Mémoires historiques sur la Louisiane.* Paris, C. J. B. Bauche, 1753.

Du Tertre, Jean Baptiste (1610–87). *Histoire générale des Isles de S. Christophe, de la Guadeloupe, de la Martinique, et autres dans l'Amérique. . . . De plus, la description de tous les animaux de la mer, de l'air, et de la terre. . . .* Paris, J. Langlois et E. Langlois, 1654.

Eastman, Charles R. "Beginnings of American Natural History," *American Museum Journal,* Vol. XV, No. 7 (November, 1915), 349–55. Also *Nature,* Vol. XCV (March 25, 1915), 89.

Eden, Richard, ed. (1521?–76). *The History of Travayle in the West and East Indies, and other countreys lying eyther way, towardes the fruitfull and ryche Moluccaes. As Moscovia, Persia, Arabia, Syria, Aegypte, Ethiopia, Guinea, China in Cathayo, and Giapan: With a discourse of the Northwest passage. In the hande of our Lorde be all the corners of the earth. Psal. 94. Gathered in parte, and done into Englyshe by Richarde Eden.* London, Richarde Iugge, 1577. Eden drew on the *Decades* of Peter Martyr.

Elze, Kurt. "Historisches über ungeborene und neugeborene Bären und die Redensart wie ein ungeleckter Bär," *Anatomischer Anzeiger, Ergänzungsheft,* Vol. XLIV (1913), 133–38. This paper, called to my attention by Herbert M. Evans, stimulated my interest in the legend.

Enders, Robert K. "Mammalian Life Histories from Barro Colorado Island, Panama." Museum of Comparative Zoology, *Bulletin,* Vol. LXXVIII, No. 4 (1935). Cambridge, Massachusetts.

———. "Panniculus carnosus and formation of the pouch in Didelphis," *Journal of Morphology,* Vol. LXI (1937), 1–26.

Fitzinger, Leopold Joseph (1802–84). *Wissenschaftlich-populäre Naturgeschichte der Säugetheire.* Vienna, 1860–61.

Geoffroy Saint-Hilaire, Étienne (1772–1844). "Memoire sur la génération des animaux à bourse et le développement de leur foetus,"

Annales des Sciences Naturelles, Ser. 1, Vol. I (1823), 392.

———. "Sur des vestiges d'organization placentaire et d'ombilic découverts chez un tres-petit foetus du Didelphys virginiana," *ibid.,* Vol. II (1824), 121–26.

Gesner, Konrad (1516–65). *Historiae animalium.* Vol. I, *De quadrupedibus viviparis.* Zurich, 1551–58.* Went through many editions. German by Forer, 1563*; English by Johnston, 1657.*

Goldsmith, Oliver (1728–74). *History of the Earth and Animated Nature.* There were many editions: first edition, London, 1774; that of 1823,* quoted herein; and the 1840* edition, which has excellent footnotes by the editor, Alexander Whitelaw.

Gudger, E. W. "Animal Carts: How Marmots, Badgers and Beavers Serve as Sleds or Wagons," *Scientific Monthly,* Vol. XL (1935), 153–57.

———. "Does the Jaguar Use His Tail as a Lure in Fishing," *Journal of Mammalogy,* Vol. XXVII, No. 1 (February, 1946), 37–49.

———. "How Rats Transport Eggs: The Rat Wagon Story Traced back to 1291 A.D.," *Scientific Monthly,* Vol. XL (1935), 415–24.

Gumilla, Joseph (d. 1750). *Historia natural, civil y geográfica de las naciones situadas en las riveras del río Orinoco.* Barcelona, 1791. French edition, *Histoire naturelle, civile et géographique de l'Orénoque.* Translated by Eidous. Paris, 1753.*

Hakluyt, Richard, ed. (1552?–1616). *The Principal Navigations.* 1582 ff. Famous collection of voyages, called "a prose epic of the English Nation." Republished and extended by Samuel Purchas, *q.v.*

Hamilton, W. J. *American Mammals.* New York, McGraw-Hill, 1939.

———. "Birth of the Opossum Family," *Natural History,* Vol. L (1942), 188–90.

Hamor, Ralph. *A True Discourse of the Present Estate of Virginia.* London, 1615. Republished by J. Munsell, Albany, 1860.

Harriot, Thomas (1560–1621). *A Briefe and True Report of the New Found Land of Virginia.* London, 1588. Republished at Frankfurt by De Bry, who added his copper engravings.

Hartman, Carl. "Studies in the Development of

the Opossum: V. The Phenomena of Parturition and the Method of Transfer of Young to the Pouch," *Anatomical Record*, Vol. XIX (1920), 1–11.

———. "Traditional Beliefs Concerning the Generation of the Opossum," *Journal of American Folk-Lore*, Vol. XXXIV (1921), 321–23.

Hediger, Heini. "Ueber einen Fall von Zahmheit bei Didelphys," *Zoologischer Garten*, Vol. VII (1934), 28–44.

———. *Wild Animals in Captivity*. London, Butterworth, 1950.

Hennepin, Louis (1640–?). *Description de la Louisiane, nouvellement découverte au sud' oüest de la Nouvelle France*. Paris, Chez la veuve Sebastien Huré, 1683.* English edition, *A New Discovery of a Vast Country in America*. London, 1698.

Hernández, Francisco (1514–78). *Cuatro libros de la naturaleza y virtudes de las plantas y animales de uso medicinal en la Nueva España, por Fr. Francisco Ximenez, 1615*. Edited by Antonio Peñafiel. Mexico City, 1888.

Hesselschwert, R. E. "Use of Den Boxes in Wildlife Restoration on Intensively Farmed Areas," *Journal of Wildlife Management*, Vol. VI (1942), 31–37.

Hill, J. P. "The Early Development of the Marsupial, with Special Reference to the Native Cat (*Dasyurus viverrinus*)," *Quarterly Journal of Microscopical Science*, Vol. LVI (1910), 1–134. This paper stimulated my first studies on the embryology of the opossum.

Hingston, R. W. G. *A Naturalist in the Guiana Forest*. London, E. Arnold and Company, 1932.

Hoagland, Hudson. "On the Mechanism of Tonic Immobility in Vertebrates," *Journal of General Physiology*, Vol. XI (1928), 715–41.

Hulme, F. Edward (1841–1909). *Natural History, Lore and Legend*. London, B. Quaritch, 1895.

Johnston, Joannes (1603-75). *De quadrupedibus*. London, 1657. Illustrated with copper plates by Matthew Merian.

Krieg, Hans. "Beobachtungen an argentinischen Beutelratten," *Zeitschrift für Morphologie und Oekologie der Tiere*, Vol. I, No. 4 (1924), 637–59.

Labrado, Sanchez. *Paraguay católico*. 1770. Quoted from Cabrera and Yepes.

Laet, Joannes de (1593–1649). *Nieuwe Wereldt, ofte Beschrijvinghe van West-Indien*. Leyden, J. Elzevier, 1625. Second edition, 1630.*

Langworthy, Orthello R. "Correlated Physiological and Morphological Studies of the Development of Electrically Responsive Areas in the Cerebral Cortex of the Opossum." Carnegie Institution of Washington, *Contributions to Embryology*, Vol. XIX, No. 103 (1927), 149–75.

Lawson, John (d. 1712). *The History of Carolina, Containing the exact description and natural history of that country*. Reprinted in 1903* by Observer Printing House, Charlotte, North Carolina, from the copy presented to the University of North Carolina by President Madison in 1831.

Lay, Daniel W. "Ecology of the Opossum in Eastern Texas," *Journal of Mammalogy*, Vol. XXIII, No. 2 (May, 1942), 147–59.

Le Page du Pratz (d. 1775). *The History of Louisiana, or of the Western Parts of Virginia and Carolina: Containing a description of the countries that lye on both sides of the river Missisipi*. London, T. Becket and P. A. De Hondt, 1763.* Translated from the French edition of 1758.

Lerius, Joannis, or Jean de Léry (1534–1611). *Historia navigationis in Brasiliam*. Geneva, E. Vignon, 1586. French edition, *Histoire d'un voyage faict en la terre du Brésil*. Edited by Paul Gaffarel. Paris, A. Lemerre, 1880.*

Le Souef, A. S., and Harry Burrell. *The Wild Animals of Australasia*. London, G. G. Harrap, 1926.

Ley, W. "Animal Fables," *Natural History*, Vol. XLVI (1940), 85–87.

Lincecum, G. "The Opossum," *American Naturalist*, Vol. VI (1872), 555–57.

Linschoten, Jan Huygen van (1563–1611). *Beschryvinghe van de gantsche Custe van Guinea . . . in Brasilien*. Amsterdam, Cornelis Claesz, 1596.

McCarthy, Frederick D. *Australian Aboriginal Decorative Art*. Sydney, Australian Museum, 1938.

———. "Pictorial Composition in Australian Aboriginal Rock Art," *Australian Museum Maga-*

zine, Vol. VII, No. 1 (June–August, 1939), 17–20.

Marcgrave, Georg (1610–44). See E. W. Gudger, "George Marcgrave, the First Student of American Natural History," *Popular Science Monthly*, September, 1912, pp. 250–74; also Postscript thereto in *Science,* October 9, 1914, pp. 507–508.

Meigs, Charles D. (1792–1869). "Memoir on the Reproduction of the Opossum, *Didelphis virginiana.*" American Philosophical Society, *Proceedings,* April, 1847.

Meredith, Louisa Anne Twamley (1812–95). *Tasmanian Friends and Foes: Feathered, Furred, and Finned.* London, M. Ward and Company, 1880.

Merian, Maria Sibylla de (1647–1717). *Histoire générale des insectes de Surinam et de toute l'Europe . . . avec autres animaux.* Paris, L. C. Desnos, 1771.* Dutch edition, 1717. A memoir on Maria Merian will be found in James Duncan's *British Moths* (1843) and in Vol. XXX of Jardine's *Naturalist's Library.*

Michel, Middleton (1822–94). "Researches on the Generation and Development of the Opossum." American Association for the Advancement of Science, *Proceedings,* Vol. III (1851), 60–63.

Moore, Carl R., and David Bodian. "Opossum Pouch Young as Experimental Material," *Anatomical Record,* Vol. LXXVI (1940), 319–27.

Münster, Sebastian (1489–1552). *Cosmographiae universalis.* Basel, Henrichum Petri, 1550. This edition is most valued. German: *Cosmographey: Das ist beschreibung aller laender, herrschafften und fuernemesten stetten des gantzen erdbodens.* Basel, 1618.

Nelson, Edward W. *Wild Animals of North America.* Washington, D. C., National Geographic Society, 1918. Illustrated by Louis Agassiz Fuertes. Track sketches by Ernest Thompson Seton.

Nierembergius, Joannis Eusebius (1595–1658). *Historia naturae, maxime peregrinae.* Antwerp, Plantiniana B. Moreti, 1635.

Olds, F. A. "A North Carolina 'Possum Hunt," *Outing,* Vol. XXXVI (1900), 33–35.

Oviedo y Valdés, Gonzalo Fernández de (1478–1557). *Coronica de las Indias.* Salamanca, Juan de Junta, 1547.

———. *OViedo dela natural hystoria delas Indias.* Toledo, Remo de Petras, 1526.

———. *Relación sumaria de la historia natural de las Indias.* Madrid, 1749. English edition by Eden, 1577,* q.v.

Owen, Richard (1804–92). "Marsupialia," in *Todd's Cyclopaedia of Anatomy and Physiology,* Vol. III. London, 1847.

Ozorio de Almeida, Miguel, and Arnoldo Rocha. "Sur la composition de l'air de la poche mammaire du Gamba." Société Biologie, *Comptes Rendus,* Vol. CIX (1932), 131.

Pelsaert, François (d. 1630). Account of the wreck of the *Batavia.* In G. J. Saeghman's *Verscheyde Oost-Indische Voyagien,* No. 18. Amsterdam, 1664.

Pennant, Thomas (1726–98). *British Zoology.* London, printed by W. Eyres, 1776–77.

———. *History of Quadrupeds.* London, 1790. Third edition, 1793.

Peter Martyr, or Pietro Martire d'Anghiera (1455–1526). *De Orbe Novo.* Alcalá, Spain. The Ninth Book of the First Decade, the part descriptive of the opossum, appeared in 1516. English edition by Eden, 1577*; German by Von Königshofer, 1582.* The translation by Francis Augustus MacNutt (London, 1912*) contains a biography of Peter Martyr with an explanation of his relation to Trevigliano.

Pinkert, Ernst. "Beobachtungen bei der Geburt eines Känguruh (*Macropus rufus*)," *Zoologischer Garten,* Vol. XXX (1888), 85–86.

Piso, Willem (1611–78). *Historia naturalis Brasiliae.* Amsterdam, L. Elzevirium, 1648.

Pray, Leon L. "Opossum Carries Leaves with Its Tail," *Journal of Mammalogy,* Vol. II (1921), 109–11.

Purchas, Samuel (1577?–1626). *Hakluytus posthumus, or Purchas his Pilgrimes.* London, 1625.* First edition, 1616. There is a reprint of the 1625 edition published by MacLehose in Glasgow, 1905–1907.

Raven, H. C. "Strange Animals of the Island Continent," *Natural History,* Vol. XXIX (1929), 83–94.

Ray, John, or Joannes Raius (1627–1705). *Synopsis methodica animalium quadrupedum et serpentini generis.* London, S. Smith and B. Walford, 1693.

Rengger, J. R. (1795–1832). *Naturgeschichte der Säugethiere von Paraguay.* Basel, Schweighausersche, 1830.

Reynolds, Harold C. "Some Aspects of the Life History and Ecology of the Opossum in Central Missouri," *Journal of Mammalogy,* Vol. XXVI, No. 4 (November, 1945), 361–79.

Rochefort, Charles (César) de (b. 1605). *Histoire naturelle et morale des iles Antilles de l'Amérique.* Rotterdam, A. Leers, 1665.

Sahagún, Bernardino de (1499–1590). *Historia general de las cosas de Nueva España.* Mexico City, A. Valdés, 1829–30.* French edition, Paris, G. Masson, 1880.*

Salley, Alexander S., ed. *Narratives of Early Carolina, 1650–1708.* New York, Scribner's, 1911. Contains "An account of the province of Carolina," by Samuel Wilson, 1682; also a similar account by Ash, *q.v.*

Schmidt-Hoendorf, F. *Birth of a Kangaroo.* Quoted in *Zoologischer Garten,* Vol. VII (1935), 223–24.

Shanafelt, Marjorie. "The Story of the Seven Stowaways," *Nature Magazine.* Vol. IX (February, 1927), 103–105.

Shaw, George (1751–1813). *General Zoology, or Systematic Natural History.* London, printed for G. Kearsley, 1800–1826.

Shetrone, Henry Clyde. *The Mound-Builders.* New York, Appleton, 1930.

Smith, Captain John (1580–1631). *A Map of Virginia.* Oxford, printed by Joseph Barnes, 1612.

———. *A True Relation.* London, printed for I. Tappe, 1608. Purchas, De Bry, Hakluyt, Harris, and other compilers copied from John Smith's works.

Smith, Luther. "An Observation on the Nest-building Behavior of the Opossum," *Journal of Mammalogy,* Vol. XXII, No. 2 (May, 1941), 201–202.

Stade, Hans, or Johannes Stadenus (1527–79). *The Captivity of Hans Stade of Hesse, in* A.D. *1547–1555, among the Wild Tribes of Eastern Brazil.* Translated by Albert Tootal. London, Hakluyt Society, 1874. Also in De

Bry, 1617.* Memoir to Hans Stade in Vol. XXIII of Jardine's *Naturalist's Library.*

———. *Hans Stadens Warhafftig Historia und beschreibung einer landtschafft der Wilden, Nacketen, Grimmigen, Menschfresser Leuthen in der Newen Welt America gelegen.* Frankfurt, 1557.*

Strachey, William (fl. 1609). *The Historie of Travaile into Virginia Britannia.* Reprint by Hakluyt Society, London, 1849.*

Tate, G. H. H. "Random Observations on Habits of South American Mammals," *Journal of Mammalogy,* Vol. XII (1931), 248–56.

Thevet, André (1502–90). *Les singularitez de la France antarctique . . . et de plusieurs terres et isles découvertes de nostre temps.* Paris, Chez les heritiers de Maurice de la Porte, 1557. Paul Gaffarel edited a reprint of the 1558 Paris edition (Paris, Maisonneuve, 1878).

Topsell, Edward (1572–1625?). *The Historie of Foure-Footed Beastes describing the true and lively Figure of every Beast . . . Collected out of all the Volumes of Conradus Gesner, and all other Writers to this Present Day.* London, printed by W. Iaggard, 1607. Revised by John Rowland, 1658.*

Trevigliano, Angelo. *Libretto di tutta la navigatione dei Rei di Spagna, delle Isole e Terreni Novamente Trovati.* Venice, 1504 ff.

Troughton, Ellis. *Furred Animals of Australia.* New York, Scribner's, 1947.

Tyson, Edward (1650–1708). *Carigueya seu Marsupiale Anerinanum: or, The Anatomy of an Opossum.* Royal Society of London, *Philosophical Transactions,* entire No. 239. 1698.

Valentyn, François (1656–1727). *Omständig Verhaal van de geschiedenissen en Zaaken . . . in Amboina, Banda oud en nieuw Oost-Indien.* Doordrecht, 1724–26.

Vogel, Howard H., Jr. "Observations on Social Behavior in Turkey Vultures," *The Auk,* Vol. LXVII (1950), 210–11.

Wafer, Lionel (1660?–1705?). *A New Voyage and Description of the Isthmus of America, giving an account of the author's abode there.* London, printed for J. Knapton, 1699.* Also in William Dampier's *A Collection of*

Voyages. London, printed for J. and J. Knapton, 1729.* Reprinted in 1903 by Burrows Brothers, Cleveland.

Waldseemüller, Martin (1470–1521?). *Cosmographiae introductio.* 1516. Contains world map, in the corner of which there is the first pictorial representation of the opossum. There is a copy of this map* in the New York Public Library.

Waterhouse, G. R. (1810–88). *A Natural History of the Mammalia.* Vol. I, *Marsupialia.* London, H. Baillière, 1846. Also in the *Royal Natural History* and in Vol. XXIV of Jardine's *Naturalist's Library.* Illustrated by colored lithographs.

Wesley, John (1703–91). *A Survey of the Wisdom of God in the Creation: or, A Compendium of Natural Philosophy.* Third American edition. With notes by B. Mayo. New York, Methodist Episcopal Church, 1823.*

Wied-Neuwied, Maximilian Alexander Philipp, Prinz von (1782–1867). *Beiträge zur Naturgeschichte Brasilien.* Weimar, Im Verlage des Landes-industrie-comptoirs, 1826.

Wood, Frank E. *Pouched Animals.* Illinois State Laboratory of Natural History, 1908–10.

Writers' Program of the W. P. A. in New York. *American Wild Life.* New York, William Wise and Company, 1940.

Index